THE
HEFTED FARMER

Susan Haywood
Barbara Crossley

Illustrations by Jocelyn Campbell and Jenny White-Cooper

HAYLOFT

First published 2004

Hayloft Publishing Ltd, Kirkby Stephen,
Cumbria, CA17 4DJ

tel: (017683) 42300
fax. (017683) 41568
e-mail: books@hayloft.org.uk
web: www.hayloft.org.uk

ISBN 1 904524 20 6

A catalogue record for this book is available
from the British Library

Produced, printed and bound in the EU

*Dedicated to the Swaledale founding fathers - a special breed
and to all those whose lives were devastated by
foot and mouth disease in 2001.*

Mr Dick Metcalfe (Patron) and Mr Clifford Harker (President to 2003) of Tan Hill Sheep Show. Both founder members of the show.

I wanted above all, to take this opportunity to salute you as part of the backbone of our precious countryside. As a consequence of the foot and mouth disaster many may have heard of hefted flocks for the first time and of the difficulty of re-establishing them once they have been removed. But do they realise that so many of you are actually hefted people - a crucial thread in the complex 'organic' tapestry that defines the essence of rural Britain? Unstitch that thread and the ancient tapestry will become featureless and abstracted; the countryside will lose that intangible element which comes from the continuity of wisdom and experience between generations.

So I pray with all my heart that a way can be found for you and your children to continue caring for our unique landscape, and the special communities which form an intricate part of it.

HRH The Prince of Wales to members of the farming community and their families at a reception held in St James's Palace on 29 January 2002.

ACKNOWLEDGMENTS
AN APPRECIATION TO ALL WHO HAVE CONTRIBUTED TO THIS BOOK

This book has been, more than anything else, the collaborative effort of friends and neighbours who have given generously and freely of their time, knowledge and expertise.

My thanks first are to Barbara Crossley, my co-author, who undertook to record the oral recollections, in particular concerning the recent foot and mouth disease epidemic, of individual members of the four farming families of upper Swaledale. In the transcriptions from these tapes she has successfully allowed their distinctive voices to contribute to a tapestry of shared experience.

Secondly, thanks to our splendid illustrators who enthusiastically volunteered their skills to the project: Jocelyn Campbell who undertook the pen and ink sketches which so skillfully evoke our wild landscape, the stone farmhouses, barns and other features of Swaledale. And Jenny White-Cooper from whose delicate pencil drawings of the view from Firs emerged together with our lovely marsh and moorland birds. Moreover, the map Jenny produced of the heafs of upper Swaledale we regard as unique since the heaf boundaries were known formerly only to the sheep!

Thirdly thank you to the four families themselves who not only supplied the foundation material of this book but were generous otherwise with their time and allowed precious family photographs and mementos to be reproduced:

To Jennie and the late Clifford Harker, once of Pry House, our nearest neighbours, who were ever friendly and helpful to us as incomers and with whom we have shared the vagaries of the spring-fed water supply to our farms! Jennie's stories of her extended family who occupied at some time nearly all of these high hill farms and particularly her grandfather Raper Whitehead, a founder member of the Swaledale Sheep Association, who settled as a young man at Ravenseat and whose memory inspired her to fight so hard to protect Swaledale and inspired me in turn to tell the story. Clifford her husband was a much liked and respected man, esteemed for his knowledge of the Swaledale sheep and he was a founder member and president of the Tan Hill Sheep Show and sadly died before the book was completed and whose farewell is incorporated in the epilogue. Thanks most particularly for allowing us to borrow those precious Flock Books! Jennie now lives in Muker and has a son Trevor, daughter Lynne and six grandchildren.

To Mr George Calvert of Hoggarths whose reminiscences could fill a book in their own right and to his wife Mabel Calvert who gently restrains and guides the flow! Their sons Raymond and Chris have now taken over the farming enterprise and have extended it to include Pry House after the death of Clifford Harker. Raymond and Alison's sons Andrew and Matthew, also are a common sight in the fields with their father. I am indebted to Raymond for useful conversation giving his actual experiences of hill farming day-by-day as recorded in this book.

To Rachel and John Hall, daughter Lisa and sons, Martin, Jonathan and Benjamin of Bridgend, Keld and whose land now includes Stonehouse pastures. Rachel's father the late Mr James Alderson of Hope House, Keld, formerly farmed Stonehouse. Theirs is a close-knit family going back many generations and includes the earlier James Alderson, a founding member of the Swaledale Sheep Association. Rachel and John have been friends and good neighbours since we first moved here and Jim Alderson shared many a tale with me most particularly concerning our mutual love of horses. I am grateful for helpful conversations, family photos and particularly thank Mrs Elenore Alderson for treasured family memorabilia including a Stonehouse flock record, a dialect poem and many old photos.

To Clive and Amanda Owen, who are more recent incumbents of Ravenseat and yet who seem as firmly embedded as if they also had come from previous generations. They too have been generous with their time (and cups of tea) and I was given my first ride on a quad bike when Clive took me round his pastures to photograph at lambing time. Forgiving and good humoured too, as shown when after having got his ram in show condition for a camera debut, I found no film in the camera! Amanda is our youngest mother in the upper dale and has given birth to a daughter Raven and a son Reuben during the course of this story, not without some drama and a bit of self help! Clive has a son Robert who helps with the farm. Amanda also helps out, time from her young family permitting; she has a particular interest in the free range poultry part of the enterprise but yet finds time for long term interest breeding coloured dual purpose horses.

I want to acknowledge the help and encouragement of Mrs Belinda Purkis and her sister Mrs Jane Nadin who are the present day owners of the Scott-Alderson Estate which incorporates Pry House and Hoggarths as well as Stone House. Although not living in Swaledale these two ladies and their families maintain a lively interest in the dale and indeed profess a deep love of their inheritance. Together with their cousin Richard Alderson Scott they have contributed to the details of the family history in this book, for which my thanks.

Nor can I forget Marie Hartley of Askrigg, an eminent local author, whose books together with her co-authors Ella Pontefract and Joan Ingleby are classics on Swaledale and its history. I am indebted to Miss Hartley for allowing me to reproduce her wood engraving *Jack o' t' Firs* for the cover of this book. Jack (John Metcalfe) is a particular favourite of mine having lived and farmed at Firs, the farmhouse lived in by my husband and myself today, and for having been one of the Swaledale founding fathers to whom we have dedicated this book.

There are other friends who have contributed directly and who are noted in the book, Martin Holdgate of Kirkby Stephen and David and

Anthea Boulton of Dent - my thanks to them. Thanks also to Jan Coates and Peter Atkinson of Park House, Keld, for making me aware of the existence of *Jack o' t' Firs* and for lending me their own print from the wood engraving. We have been most grateful for two poems written in the aftermath of the foot and mouth epidemic by two ladies from Arkengarthdale, Vivienne Metcalf and Elizabeth Sutherland, to them our thanks. Many other friends and family have encouraged by their support and enthusiasm for the project and to them and to anyone that I have overlooked, also my thanks.

My most grateful thanks to my husband, George Graham Haywood, whose constant support and encouragement during the gestation of this book has been much appreciated. His knowledgeable reading of, and suggestions for, the text have been invaluable as has been his technical expertise with my word processing and photo-scanning facilities. Finally for acting as midwife during the delivery of the completed manuscript to our publishers, for all these things my gratitude goes beyond praise!

I should like to acknowledge and thank Dawn Robertson of Hayloft Publishing Ltd for, in addition to her editorial skills, her enthusiasm, knowledge and empathy for the subject of this book.

This appreciation is not complete without including His Royal Highness Prince Charles the Prince of Wales whose steadfast support during the dark days of 2001 gave us the courage to fight on. We thank him for permission to reproduce the letter sent by his office to Mrs Jennie Harker at this time. We also thank him for providing the text of his address at a reception he gave to farmers and their families held at St James's Palace on 29 January 2002 and from which I took the idea of the title for this book.

Susan Haywood, September 2004

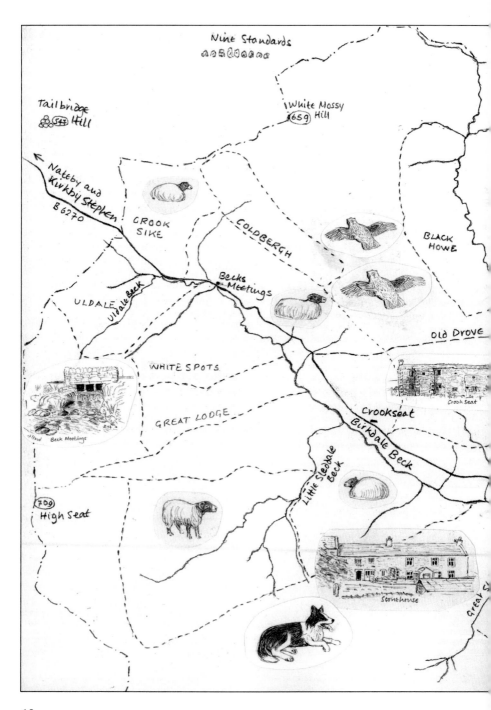

Nine Standards

Tailbridge Hill

White Mossy (659) Hill

Nateby and Kirkby Stephen B6270

CROOK SIKE

COLDBERGH

BLACK HOWE

Becks Meetings

ULDALE Uldale Beck

Old Drove

WHITE SPOTS

Crookseat

Crook Seat

GREAT LODGE

Birkdale Beck

Beck Meetings

Little Sleddale Beck

(709) High Seat

Stonehouse

Great Sl

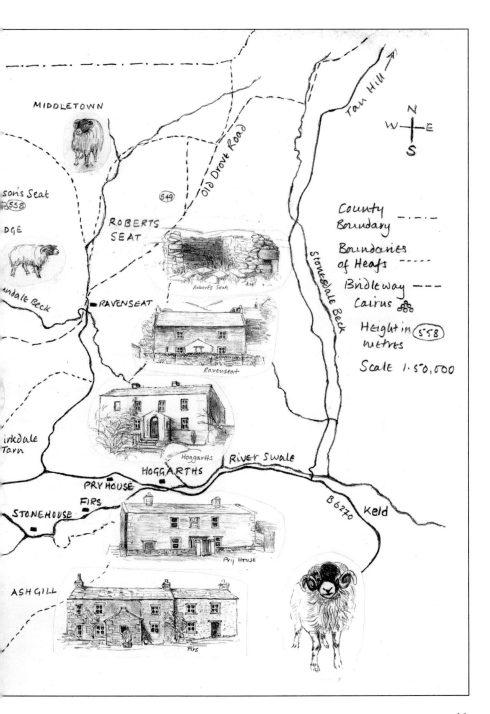

MIDDLETOWN

...son's Seat
558

DGE

...ndale Beck

...irkdale Tarn

ROBERTS SEAT

RAVENSEAT

Roberts Seat

Ravenseat

Hoggarths

HOGGARTHS

PRY HOUSE
FIRS

STONEHOUSE

Pry House

ASHGILL

Firs

Old Drove Road

549

Stonesdale Beck

River Swale

B6270   Keld

Tan Hill

N
W   E
S

County
Boundary   —·—·—

Boundaries
of Heafs   -----

Bridleway   -----
Cairns   &

Height in   558
metres

Scale 1·50,000

11

About the Authors:

SUSAN Haywood is a veterinary pathologist who has spent her professional life teaching vet students at Liverpool University. She lives in Swaledale with her husband and divides her time between looking after her flock of rare-breed, North Ronaldsay sheep, her fell ponies, two dogs and two barn cats, as well as maintaining a part-time research position at the university. Besides her scientific writing she has written for journals and newspapers during the recent (2001) foot and mouth disease epidemic.

Barbara Crossley has always been very interested in all kinds of social history, and fifteen years ago joined the Ambleside Oral History Society, one of the oldest in the country. She wrote a book, called *The Other Ambleside* published in 2000, which draws on life in the community.

About the illustrators:

JOCELYN Campbell is an artist who lived in Muker for a period of her youth and illustrated the book on the history of Muker by Edmund Cooper, her father. She has latterly published a book of her own water colour paintings *A Fountain of Gardens* and now lives in Arkengarthdale.

Jenny White-Cooper is a sign writer and calligrapher who lives in Kirkby Stephen and has recently written and illustrated a childrens book *A Likely Tale.*

CONTENTS

Jack o' t' Firs

The fireplace, lustrous with the polishing of generations, occupies nearly the length of one side, and from its glowing fire comes the fragrant odour of peat. In an arm-chair before it the farmer smokes his clay pipe, and watches the kettle hanging from a steel bar and hook, which slides on a crane along the top of the fireplace.

A farmhouse kitchen, Firs, circa 1932, from *Swaledale* by Ella Pontefract and Marie Hartley

'Jack o' t' Firs' from an original wood engraving by Marie Hartley.

View from Firs

I
INTRODUCTION

Ilook out from my window at Firs in upper Swaledale, onto a scene which has changed little since John Metcalfe (Jack o' t' Firs) viewed it some seventy years ago. Swaledale, the most northerly of the Yorkshire dales and arguably the most beautiful, opens out before me. Green pastures bounded by dry stone walls, fall steeply from the gently rounded hills down to the valley bottom. Each field has its own stone barn, a unique feature of this dale, built over three hundred years ago for the wintering of animals and storage of fodder. In late June the meadows are a rich tapestry of wild flowers, the hay made from them a perfumed reminder of summer during the long dark days of winter. This happy co-existence of man and nature is maintained by the largely traditional farming practised here - the breeding and rearing of the heafed Swaledale sheep.

Running through it all is the river Swale, the so-called 'fast flowing' river, which tumbles through ravines or meanders along the valley bottom and is criss-crossed by innumerable bridges of the same remarkable construction as the barns and farmhouses. The river Swale was once named the Holy River for the number of people baptised in it by Paulinus in the seventh century AD, a practice claimed to have been performed still in living memory by some dwellers of the upper reaches of the Swale - though surely no longer.

I can see one of these bridges as I write. This is a beautifully constructed bridge, which includes a date stone 1840. It describes a lovely arc across the Swale, and although it seems not to go to or from anywhere, it actually carries a footpath that may once have been a pack pony route from a nearby long-disbanded lead mine, Loanin End. But this bridge has for me another, deeper meaning; it represents the link uniting man and nature in these parts which enables their mutual well being.

In the terrible summer of 2001, Swaledale was nearly changed forever when foot and mouth disease struck the northern counties and the demands of commerce and heritage came into conflict. It came home to us then how very fragile was this lovely dale, despite the supposed protection of agencies which included the North Yorkshire National Park and English Nature among others, in the face of trade and centralised control. There seemed insufficient understanding that the survival and continuation of the dale depended on the traditional farming pursued in these uplands. Indeed, we heard it stated that the sheep were 'just another interest group' among many! In truth, if the hefted sheep were to go, they would not return, the traditional economy would disappear and with it the farming way of life and the face of this countryside would change forever.

This is a tale of the farming families of the upper dale, breeders of the pedigree Swaledale sheep, whose forebears established the breed. It is a celebration of these farmers of the northern uplands who for generations have reared a unique breed of sheep and who have farmed using mainly traditional methods to the preservation and enhancement of the natural landscape. These people, who despite losing much and who nearly lost everything, coped with resilience and fortitude, and are now fighting back to preserve and to pass on their unique heritage. This book is a chance for them to tell in their own voices something of their lives, the good and bad times and, in particular, the near elimination of their way of life during the foot and mouth epidemic of 2001. We hope to show to a wider, and mainly urban, audience that the maintenance of the countryside as a sustainable habitat for wildlife and for human enjoyment is inseparable from the non-intensive traditional farming practised in these regions. Their relationship with the land and the animals it supports, who in turn support us, unsentimental and yet respectful, is one that was common up to a short time ago, but with increased urbanisation this link has been severed and now it is all but lost. To work with nature is surely the oldest relationship of all and one which must be renewed and cherished.

We hope the individual voices of our farmers will speak directly, and that their unique contribution to our heritage be recognised and valued by all.

SH. Firs 2003

Stone house in winter, Dale Head

The County Boundary

2
HEAFS AND HILL FARMS

The sweep of the North Pennines from the promontories of Tailbridge Hill and Nine Standards Rigg in the north-west across to Bowes moor and Arkengarthdale in the east, is the ancestral home of the hefted Swaledale sheep, whose characteristics have been formed by the harshness and isolation of the region. These commanding heights take in an area of wild fell more than two thousand feet above sea level. Tan Hill Inn, which claims to be the highest public house in Britain is situated in the heart of these fells, and hosts the annual Swaledale sheep show. To the west stretches the aptly named Eden valley, in what was once Westmorland but is now Cumbria, with Kirkby Stephen at its head. Kirkby Stephen is a working community with its active auction mart giving evidence of the importance of sheep rearing to the economy of this region. To the south-east is Swaledale in North Yorkshire with its tributary valleys of Sleddale and Birkdale, Whitsundale, Weststonesdale and Arkengarthdale leading the eye down towards Muker, Reeth, Richmond and beyond.

This region, little more than fifteen miles long, includes the working hill farms which, though reduced in number, still breed and rear the Swaledale sheep, in ways little changed from that practised by their

Uldale heafed Swaledales

forebears. The dispersed stone farmsteads, though often above a thousand feet, are generally built in the more sheltered parts of the hill side or valley bottoms and are surrounded by pasture land, broken up into fields enclosed by the characteristic dry stone walls of this region. A feature, which is unique to this region, is that every field has its own stone barn built for the storage of hay and the wintering of stock. Taken overall, the picture presents a busy mosaic of patterned fields and barns. This particular farming practice may follow the tradition of the early Norse settlers whose heritage is still so marked in the place names, dialect and appearance of the dales men and women.

Integral and essential to the success of farming in this dale is the tradition of hefting or heafing the sheep whereby each farm retains access, as of right, to defined areas of unfenced fell, known as heafs.

The source of the word 'heaf' and the adjective 'hefted' or 'heafed', which is pronounced 'heeafed' in Swaledale dialect (see *Men of Swaledale* by Edmund Cooper) or alternatively 'heughed' (see *A Dales Heritage* by Marie Hartley and Joan Ingilby), is not fully understood. *The Cumbrian Dictionary of Dialect Tradition and Folklore* (William

Rollinson, Smith, Settle Ltd., 1997) definition, supplied by Mrs Jenny White-Cooper of Kirkby Stephen states, 'Heaf: the portion of fell farm as sheep pasture; a sheep walk. Heaf-gangen or hefted sheep are animals which are let along with the farm and pastured on a particular heaf,' but gives no derivation for the word.

A. H. Smith, 1966, in *The place names of Westmorland*, goes further and cites 'hefe', 'heaf' as early modern English dialect for 'regular pasture for sheep' and cross-refers to Heaves (Levens) as a place name first referred to in 1737 and again in 1815 saying, 'there was here an ancient enclosure possibly where sheep were examined or regularly pastured.' This still leaves us without a derivation. Martin Holdgate of Hartley, Kirkby Stephen, to whom I am indebted for the foregoing information, wonders whether heaf could be related to the Old English heafod which is widely used hereabout to mean 'head, headland, end of a ridge, upper end, river source, head of a valley.' He surmises that, 'a heaf, after all, is commonly bound by just such features.'

The origins of the practice of hefting can only be speculated, but Martin cites Pearson and Pennington, in their New Naturalist volume, *The Lake District* (1973) who say that while sheep husbandry was almost certainly a feature of the area in Norse times (and the Herdwick strain may owe something genetically to Norse sheep), it was the Cistercian monks who converted large tracts of fell country into sheep pasture. These authors suggest that it was in the period from around 1300 to 1800 AD that this widespread sheep pasturage eroded the woodlands, and set in motion ecological changes that created the landscape we know today. At the same time, they mention the strong homing instinct of the Herdwick sheep, 'which usually keeps it on its own heaf on these unenclosed fells.' Anecdotally, this is true also of the Swaledale sheep. Tales abound to the fact that, not only do the sheep tend to keep to their own heaf on which they were born, and even travel many miles to return if taken away, but also some ewes will mark very particular local territories as their own - a headland, a crag, a river bank - so that farmers can always locate them and their lambs should they become missing from the main flock.

Further research by Anthea and David Boulton of Dent has thrown up the following from the *Old English Dictionary* (1933 edition) which says that heaf is, 'a northern dialect modification of heft, haft, accustomed pasture ground (of sheep).' Furthermore, 'a connection suggests itself

Crook Seat

with G[erman] heften to fasten, attach, OS [Old Saxon] heftian to make fast; i.e. to establish in a situation or place of residence, to locate, fix, specifically to accustom (sheep, cattle) to a pasturage.'

And there we rest this enquiry. Whatever the origins and associations, a heaf typically consists of approximately a hundred hectares of unfenced fell, generally one to two thousand feet above sea level, bounded by becks (streams) or other natural features and supporting between one hundred and one hundred and fifty sheep. These numbers of sheep appear to be 'manageable blocks' that can be treated as a group by a shepherd and his dogs, and also presumably an optimum group in which member sheep can recognise other members of the flock, thus retaining its identity. The adult ewes are still kept out on their own heaf throughout the year. They once would have had to 'make do' with whatever sparse vegetation they could forage in winter, but nowadays they are fed hay or silage and, before lambing, energy-rich concentrates. Seemingly they have a more pampered life in the twenty-first century!

Access to Swaledale from Cumbria in the west, is by means of the B6270 road which starts from the small hamlet of Nateby near Kirkby Stephen. The road ascends east for four miles up the fellside of Nateby Common, and is flanked on the right by the commanding presence of High Seat (2,326 feet), and on the left it is in sight of Nine Standards

Rigg (2,170 feet), a lookout post of antiquity. It reaches its highest point of 1,625 feet above sea level with a last push up the one in five of Tailbridge Hill (or Tail Briggs as it's sometimes called). A short distance along from there and the Cumbria/Yorkshire boundary is announced by road signs and, more prominently, a stone bearing the handsome head of a Swaledale ram or tup. For make no mistake this is the land of the Swaledale sheep and few county boundaries can be so demarcated.

The wide expanse of open moor has few distinguishing features. The treeless landscape covered by the wiry moorland grass is broken only by the peat haggs which disclose deep banks of peat laid down by rotting vegetation and preserved by the acidity of the soil in former times. The colour of the moor changes subtly with the seasons; it shows green only after early May and gradually assumes a deep russet at the onset of autumn which when clothed with snow makes a fine picture.

Barn, Birkdale

This bare moor is the site of the heafs, the unmarked territories of generations of sheep that graze within their boundaries. The sheep can be seen dotted over the hillsides or in small groups by the roadside in winter where they are fed. The lambs learn from their dams the extent of their territories and rarely stray, each heaf being home to successive generations of sheep with their own distinct characteristics.

The heafs with which this story is concerned are not necessarily attached to the 'in bye', that is the enclosed pasture land around their respective farmsteads, but may be at some distance away as the map (on pages 10 and 11) shows. The sheep reared on the fells of upper Swaledale are direct descendants of the original Swaledale sheep which were first bred on these bleak Pennine hills and which now can be found throughout the North of England. The four farms which are still farmed today and play the leading part in this story are Stonehouse at the head of the dale, Pry House and Hoggarths, near neighbours on the road to Keld, and Ravenseat a mile away up Whitsundale and enclosed by hills. Each farm has about one hundred acres of enclosed pasture and meadowland directly attached or at a short distance from the farm in addition to the heafed fell. The farms are owned by the estate owners and let to farming tenants. It is important to realise that the heafed sheep are passed on with the tenancy and so each farmer in turn takes on a going concern. The incumbent tenants may be part of a family tradition going back several generations as is the case with the Alderson family (now Hall) of Stonehouse and the Calverts of Hoggarths.

Bridge at Becks Meeting

Alternatively today's farmers may well have undertaken the tenancy in more recent times such as is the case with the Harkers of Pry House and the Owens of Ravenseat. Both these latter families, however, have come from farming stock; indeed Jennie Harker's grandfather, Raper Clarkson Whitehead originally of Ravenseat, was a founder member of the Swaledale Sheep Breeders' Society as was Rachel Hall's grandfather, James Alderson. People have not moved much from the dale and family names occur again and again throughout the generations. The 'Aldersons' probably hark back to the original Norse settlers over a thousand years ago! These people are well hefted indeed!

The heafs have individual names, derived from distinguishing geographical features. Starting from the county boundary on Birkdale Common, we see Uldale to the right with Crook Sike to the left of the B6270, itself merging onto the steep incline of Coldbergh side. These three heafs belong to Stonehouse formerly farmed by James Alderson of Keld but now by his daughter Rachel Hall and her husband John Hall also of Keld.

Moving eastwards barely half a mile along the road we come to Becks Meeting, a confluence of becks over which the road passes; the two becks become Birkdale Beck. This inconspicuous bridge crossing is frequently flooded after heavy rain when the beck becomes a torrent. From there on the right hand side or 'black side' of the fell, so designated by the heather moors which appear black in winter, are the heafs of Whitespots Gutter and Lodge Gill grazed by the Pry House sheep belonging to Clifford and Jennie Harker.

This boundary is given further emphasis by the existence of a roofed stone sheepfold, Black Scar House or as it is known locally, Becks Meeting House. This sheepfold is shared by two farmers and is used for 'gathering', dipping and shearing the sheep. In earlier times, a shepherd would have taken up temporary residence, and made up a fire here for branding the sheep with each owner's distinctive mark. Nowadays the sheep are 'colour coded', each bearing a particular farm mark in addition to the individual heaf mark. Despite all precautions sheep do get mixed up from time to time and shepherds' meets were held in July and November at local hostelries such as the Black Bull Inn, Nateby or Tan Hill Inn on the top of Stonesdale moor to exchange sheep that had wandered. Needless to say these were social occasions and the Tan Hill Show has arisen from earlier meets.

Becks Meeting House

Roofed sheep folds like Becks Meeting House are to be found commonly throughout the dale by the becks or water and serve a similar purpose. Sometimes buildings now used for sheep were once inhabited, such is the case at Crook Seat on the main B6270 road. Smaller stone built enclosures shown as sheep folds and marked on Ordnance Survey maps are commonly seen on the fell. They are known locally as 'laying folds', 'liggin folds' or 'liggins' and were built in times past for shelter from the harsh weather on the treeless fells. Notably the older sheep, sensing oncoming bad weather, would gather in these shelters, sometimes twenty-four hours or more before the onset of the storm. The same holds true today and this practise is reinforced by using them as foddering sites in winter.

Pry House sheep are also heafed to the left side or the 'white side' of the fell, so named because of the lack of heather. The remainder of Birkdale Common eastwards and southwards up to the boundary at over two thousand feet is heafed fell attached to Hoggarths and farmed by the Calvert family, once Mr and Mrs George Calvert but now by their two sons Raymond and Chris Calvert, of Hoggarths on the road to Keld. These particular heafs include a wide tract of fell and take in Little Sleddale Beck and its tributaries before joining Birkdale Beck on its journey to merge with Great Sleddale Beck just beyond Stonehouse and to form the River Swale.

Stonehouse is situated at Dalehead in upper Swaledale and the heft on

Ashgill side on the far side of Great Sleddale Beck is contiguous with the home pastures. Stonehouse, long farmed by the Alderson family (now Hall), belongs to the Scott-Alderson estate. This estate is also the landlord for both Pry House and Hoggarths, whereas Ravenseat belongs to the Miller estate (formerly Lord Peel's estate).

The family history tells us that Stonehouse, its barns and outbuildings are the amalgamation of several farms near this site. Two unmarried brothers, George and Charles Alderson, were yeoman farmers at Stonehouse for some forty years and took every opportunity to buy up local farms and land in the mid 1800s. They built Pry farmhouse in 1858 and subsequently split the land they owned between it and Stonehouse. Charles died in 1866 and thereafter George moved to Pry, leasing Stonehouse to a cousin (John Alderson, Rachel Hall's great grandfather). When George died in 1876, Pry was also let but the ownership of both it and Stonehouse passed to George's grandson, George Alderson-Scott, the present owner's grandfather. In the meantime George Alderson's son had moved away to London. He bought Hoggarths and that too was inherited by George Alderson-Scott on his father's early death in 1885.

Liggin fold, Crook Seat

The buildings are in an excellent state of repair and include barns and sheepfolds, together with another splendid bridge built by a forebear. A digression at this point is worthwhile since the home pastures are well delineated by stone walls; each pasture contains a stone barn: a unique feature of Swaledale. These have been mentioned previously and were for the over-wintering of cattle and the young sheep (hoggs). They are splendid examples of dry-stone walled structures built as they were

Stonehouse

without mortar or cement but relying on their ingenious double-walled construction with binding stone 'infill'. They have projecting 'throughs' or 'wet stones' for directing rain water away from the interiors which might freeze and cause later damage. Overall the barns are roofed with local sandstone slates which are plentiful in the river beds around.

The resilience of these structures can be appreciated from the carved dates that are frequently from the late seventeenth and early eighteenth centuries, a period of agricultural prosperity. Only recently have they needed a programme of maintenance when the roof timbers finally began to give way. A peek into their interiors reveals that sometimes these barns are two-storied and built into the hill, the intervening division being made of stone flags like the roof. This was because the upper storey was used for sheep whilst cattle and/or fodder was in the lower storey. The barns are not used so much as formerly but are retained for shelter and sometimes for storage, and most particularly for their unique contribution to our agricultural heritage.

Elsewhere the heafs belonging to the Hall family are widely spread. In addition to Ashgill at Stonehouse there is Moor Close, down by Thwaite, which belongs to the family of Cherry Kearton; and Greenses which is owned by Mrs Calvert of Gunnerside.

Ravenseat is at the head of Whitsundale, a mile north from the B6270 road. It is the most remote of the farms of the upper dale, but possibly the most contained in that the heafs rise directly from the enclosed pastures up the fellside. Four main contiguous heafs remain populated and are named Black Howe, Side Edge on Ravenseat moor, Middletown and Robert's Seat. Once more these heafs are delineated by natural features, becks, watersheds and also by county boundaries. These latter have been the cause of friction between the Yorkshire and Westmorland shepherds in times past and White Mossy hill was the subject of a legal dispute in the late nineteenth century after several violent confrontations. This heaf and some others have been depopulated deliberately to encourage the grouse and perhaps to reduce tensions!

Ravenseat has a long history. As well as the farmhouse and outbuildings, there are a few cottages. These were once for the farm workers to live in, but now lodge the gamekeepers of the estate. Long ago there was an inn here to serve the needs of drovers who made the journey from Tan Hill colliery over the moor and the picturesque bridge is a reminder of those times. Also there was a Nonconformist Inghamite chapel and the windows of one of the outhouses can be seen as witness its earlier use. The whole sits snugly at the head of Whitsundale in the fold of the surrounding hills, with Robert's Seat to the right and Alderson Seat to the left.

Finally, what's in a name? Is this romantic place really the seat of ravens? I do know that we have seen one, and have indeed rescued and identified a young raven which was temporarily concussed on the near-by road a few years ago! Clive Owen confirms that ravens can sometimes be heard circling overhead at night uttering their characteristic

Ravenseat

29

harsh cry, 'a bark like a dog.' Where they nest though appears elusive which is perhaps just as well!

The pasture on these fells is generally acidic although with small limestone outcrops. It includes rough pasture on which grows the hardiest and often least nutritious grasses such as purple moor grass (*Molinia caerulia*) and mat grass (*Nardus stricta*); peat bogs with sphagnum moss; heather and occasionally bilberry. Bracken occurs but is uncommon - a major benefit because it can harbour the ticks with the organisms which cause Lyme disease, increasingly prevalent in sheep, dogs and even man in other parts of the country. The heather is a good source of nutrition for sheep; this causes a bone of contention for it is also a delicacy for grouse too, leading to head-on clashes of interested groups.

These northern fells include some of the finest grouse moors in England and, being managed for sportsmen, are a source of income for the estate owners. The problem is that grouse numbers have been declining in the past years, directly proportional, it is claimed, to the increase

Barn with stone ceiling

in sheep numbers on the fell and to the decline of the heather. In particular, the chicks are said to rely on the young heather shoots in April when food is scarce and the climate can be particularly hostile. This conflict of interests has lead to a reduction of sheep on the fells in schemes introduced by English Nature whereby a proportion of the young sheep, the hoggs, are removed and overwintered on the lowlands to allow the regeneration of the heather stocks. More drastic has been the complete removal of some of the hefted sheep by reclaiming or buying the rights to particular heafs. This has caused a 'loosening up' of the hefting system whereby heafs which were once contiguous with neighbouring heafs are now often separated by open moor; with a resulting tendency for a flock to expand its territory!

Needless to say the farmers have different opinions as to the merits of the heather regeneration and corresponding sheep depletion, schemes! It is worth noting though that, as Raymond Calvert of Hoggarths vehemently affirms, a balance between sheep grazing and grouse rearing is essential to maintain optimal conditions for both. Birkdale Common is now, in his opinion, under-grazed with the heather growing high, tough and woody - of little use to neither beast nor bird! This necessitates quite extensive annual burning to encourage new growth for the young grouse. He maintains that careful grazing keeps the heather from growing too woody and burning may only be necessary every four years or so. Furthermore he states that he has observed that young grouse chicks are more common where there are sheep, or more particularly sheep droppings, since he claims that the grouse chicks feed on small insects and other invertebrates present in the dung. This is an interesting observation since although grouse are claimed traditionally to feed on vegetable matter, the order to which they belong, *Galliformes*, are said to feed on small insects in addition to shoots and seeds. It is a subject well worth investigating further since field observations like this have always been the backbone of later more academic studies.

In this regard it is questionable whether the grouse have recovered their numbers since the removal of the sheep. Recently the failure to re-establish has been blamed on a parasitic disease affecting their populations. However, it was noted more than fifty years ago that grouse numbers underwent a periodic decline as a result of overstocking, the so-called 'grouse disease', and that populations were naturally maintained by such methods in the absence of wild predators, themselves controlled by game keepers. Perhaps it is that grouse as a wild indigenous species enjoy a niche with grazing hefted sheep in the ecology of the region, thriving on their extensive habitat and not taking kindly to attempts at more intensive methods of rearing? Perhaps the Swaledale sheep on their heafs are essential to maintaining the very viability of this most acclaimed of game birds?

*'Close Hills Favourite' B 1319, Sire B 309
Lambed 1928. Winner of the Swaledale Challenge Cup at Bowes, also of the
'Harcla' Challenge Cup and Sir F Melbank's prize for the best Swaledale Ram
at Kirkby Stephen Show, and 1st for best Ram at Grains-o-Beck, all in 1929.
Bred and owned by Mr R C Whitehead, Ravenseat, Keld.*

Line up at Swaledale sheep show, circa 1924

3
ORIGINS OF THE SWALEDALE SHEEP

In the early years of the twentieth century Raper Whitehead of Arkengarthdale heard of a farm to let in upper Swaledale complete with the local hefted sheep. He was seventeen years old and together with his mother, his younger siblings and all their worldly goods piled into a horse-drawn cart, the family set off over the moors to Ravenseat farm to take possession. The route he travelled was even then a rough drovers' road barely distinguished from the always encroaching moor-land and, in bad weather, the ever present peat bogs were a trap for the unwary. Nowadays, a footpath is marked on the map but it is indiscernible on the moor for the most part. It crosses the wide expanse of Stonesdale moor, past Robert's Seat House, a one time game keeper's shelter to Tan Hill inn before going on to Arkengarthdale.

After his epic journey the young man set up house with his mother and the rest of the family, and concentrated his mind on the sheep which were to be the mainstay of the farming enterprise, although in those days he would have milk cows for the home farm. These shorthorns would provide milk for family consumption; and there would be enough to make into butter and cheese for sale at the market at Muker. The sheep were

'Close Hills White Heather,' B 166 (Vol. 3, page 31), Sire B 36 Bred and owned by Mr R C Whitehead, Ravenseat, Keld. 1st Open and District Shearling Classes, Swaledale Agric. Show, 1922; 1st Open and District Aged Classes, Swaledale Agric. Show, 1923, and also 1924. Champion Male Sheep at the same Show in 1924. 1st (Aged) Muker Ram Show and Sale, 1924, at which it was sold for £51 to Mrs Dargue, Forest Hall, Kendal.

particularly hardy - they had to be! The winters were long and hard, and the fells which supported them, when not snowbound, were lashed by heavy rain for weeks on end. They were also good mothers, protecting their lambs when they were at their most vulnerable, and nature sometimes at its most cruel. Raper Whitehead soon appreciated the sterling qualities of the sheep he had inherited with the farm, and together with similarly interested neighbours they decided to register these sheep of the Northern Pennines as a distinct breed in 1919; recording, maintaining and improving their characteristics for all time.

On the 10 May 1920 the Swaledale Dalesbred Sheep Breeders' Association was inaugurated at a meeting of interested farmers in Kirkby Stephen. The first volume of the Flockbook records that the sheep were: 'noted for purity, a breed bold and hard... well filled to endure hardships of exposed and high-lying situations. Ewes are excellent lamb rearers and being good feeders and of strong constitution, they are unsurpassed as mutton producers.'

The area covered was originally formed into three districts. District A was Barnard Castle and included Teesdale and Weardale; district B took in Swaledale; and district C covered Kirkby Stephen.

Founder members of the Swaledale district were recorded as:

Raper Whitehead of Ravenseat, Keld

James Alderson of Stonehouse

George Clarkson of Pry house

Chris Calvert of Hoggarths

John Metcalfe of Firs

James Alderson, missed the birth of his daughter Margaret to attend this meeting so Rachel Hall, his grand daughter, told me.

These farms are the very ones which form the subject of this book and with the exception of Firs their occupants still farm and maintain the Swaledale sheep. Some of them indeed are descendants of the original founders!

In 1923 the 'Dalesbred' designation was dropped and the Swaledale Sheep Breeders' Association came into being, with the incorporation of some additional districts, these being District D, St. John's Chapel (Weardale) and District E, North York Moors.

Swaledale Dales-bred Ram, the property of John Lawrence Peacock, Punchard House. First Prize Winner at Royal Show, Darlington, 1920.

35

Stonehouse tups, 1924

'Steeane hoose' (Stonehouse) Hero, 1924

Dialect Rhyme — No. 4.

"SWO'DIL TEEUPS II."

(To JOHN ALDERSON, Muker).

" WELL Meg, mi lass," said Matt, "Ah've been
   Te t' Teeup Showe an' Seeale ;
It just caps aw Creation, lass,
   It licks a Fairy teeale.

" Ah bowt a Catalogue, fer yance
   (Ah'd Tuppince *thaur* te pay) ;
They've gi'en the'r Teeups the grandist neeames,
   Whaur *can* they git 'em fra?

" The'r up-te-date, an' aw, lass,
   They keep weel oot o' t' rut ;
Ther's yan caw'd 'Muker Fashion,'
   An' another 'Swalehead Nut.'

" Ther's 'Samson' an' ther's 'Buffalo Bill,'
   Beeath fit fer anny flock ;
Ther's 'Moss Rose,' 'Snowdrop,' 'Shamrock,' —
   He's t' pick o' t' Pry Hoose Stock.

" Ther's 'Bonnie Feeace' an' 'Bonnie Legs,'
   Ther's 'Cropper,' 'Ranger,' 'Mettle ;'
Ther's 'Prince,' an' 'Duke,' an' 'Tommy Top,'
   An' aw i' tip-top fettle.

" Ther's 'Swell,' an' 'Swagger,' an' 'Surprise,' —
   The best o' Stooansdil blood ;
Ther's 'Little John,' an' aw, lass,
   But neea bowld 'Robin Hood.'

"As Edwin knocked 'em doon, lass,
   Yan felt a lile bit stunned
When Steeane Hoose Sheearin, 'Hero,'
   Was seld fer Eighty Pund.

"T' best o' Yowes er Queens, lass,
   The'r Crooned, an' weel they pay ;
An' t' Teeup 'at's bred i' Swo'dil Heead
   Is t' King o' Teeups te-day."

Hawes, 1925

J. THWAITE

Swaledale Wool in Tweeds

The Story of

Westmorland Tweed

Made from 100% genuine
Swaledale Wool

by

Braithwaite & Co. Ltd
Mealbank Mill
Kendal

Some six hundred years ago the English Woollen Industry came into being and it was in Kendal, in Westmorland, that the real development took place.

The abundant supply of wool from the local sheep - much of which had previously been exported - attracted the attention of John Kempe, a Flemish woollen manufacturer. In 1331 he was granted a 'Letter of Protection' which enabled him to establish himself and his trade. He brought his knowledge and a number of Flemish weavers and other operatives to the district, and the Kendal Coat of Arms with the motto *Pannus Mihi Panis* (Wool is my Bread) testifies to the success he achieved.

In Westmorland there rises the River Swale, and this gives its name to another notable connection with the woollen trade - the Swaledale sheep, the wool of which is used for the manufacture of Westmorland Tweeds.

At Meal Bank Mills, just outside Kendal, these tweeds have their origin, and they have found their way into many parts of the world. These mills have been running for some two hundred years and since 1834 have been in the same family of which the fifth generation is now in active evidence.

Swaledale wool which has a character of its own has been found to be eminently suitable for the manufacture of high quality, hard wearing tweeds. Although various other types of wool have been tried out in blends with Swaledale when there has been a shortage of supply, no substitution for the pure Swaledale has proved satisfactory.

In order that members and others who may be interested may have the opportunity of examining these fabrics, arrangements are being made with the cooperation of the Swaledale Breeders' Association for them to be exhibited at the suitable Agricultural Shows.

'Close Hills Mountain Boy', B 1585, Sire B 1092, GS, B 548
Winner of the Swaledale Challenge Cup at Bowes Agricultural Show in 1930.
Bred and owned by Mr Raper Whitehead, Ravenseat, Keld.

Lambing records, Stonehouse, 1921

'Pennington Swell,' A 1115, Sire C 553, GS, B 429, GGS, B14 2nd prize at the Royal Show, Harrogate, 1929. 1st at Royal Show, Manchester, 1930, Aged Ram Class and Reserve for Champion prize. In 1928 this Ram was 1st Great Yorks. Show, Halifax; 1st at Barnard Castle, 1st and Champion prize at St. Johns Chapel, 1st at Middleton-in-Teesdale, and 1st and Champion prize at Wolsingham. Bred by Sir F Milbank, Bart. - and the property of Mr Jos. W Dent, Fair View, Middleton-in-Teesdale.

Swaledale Ewes. Winners of the First prize at the Royal Show, Harrogate, 1929. Bred and owned by Mr J W Dent, Fair View, Middleton-in-Teesdale.

The brand or mark of the Association consists of a Crown, that must be inspected by members of the Association.

It is interesting to read the specification of the breed as laid down in the first volume of the Flockbook:

Head to be of medium length and strong in feature with a tuft of wool on the forehead. The upper part of the face is dark complexioned and the lower part grey or mealey. Eyes quick and bright, hairs on face short and strong with a deep jaw and short broad teeth.

Horns: low set, round and rather wide

Ears: grey and of medium length.

Wool: white except back of head with a thick deep bed and a curly top, medium length, not coarse and hangs down shanks. Wool has a good 'bind' and fills hands well.

Body: medium length of neck, shoulders medium with well rounded ribs, chest well let down, broad level back, good firm loins, long drawn hind quarters and full in thigh.

Tail: long and woolly.

Legs: good flat bone of medium length, well set and with well-shaped hocks. Grey or mottled and with good sized feet.

Swaledale ewes, bred and owned by Mr G W Dent, Bleathgill, Stainmore. Winners at Penrith, Ousby and Culgaith, Brough, Kirkby Stephen and Bowes Agricultural Shows in 1926.

Over the years there has been change mostly dominated by the markets. There is no head tuft and the wool particularly is much shorter having been bred out due principally to the failure of the wool market. Once upon a time Swaledale wool was found eminently suitable for the manufacture of high quality, hard wearing tweeds and was much in demand. Nowadays the chief demand of the Swaledale is for crossing with the Blue-faced Leicester to produce a mule which has all the mothering qualities and hardiness of the Swaledale, but with the larger frame and prolificacy of the Leicester to make the ideal lowland sheep.

The original specifications have been retained within the current Flockbooks and all today's sheep can be traced to their original ancestry.

A quick glance at the old lambing records shows that each and every sheep was known and recorded by its individual characteristics - 'grey face clout,' 'black buttock,' 'nobby shag' and 'greasley grey nose.' Quite an undertaking with 500 sheep!

James Alderson of Stonehouse circa 1975, copyright Yorkshire Post.

4

THE HILL FARMER'S YEAR

Farming is carried on much as formerly except that rearing milk cows has been replaced by beef cattle, chiefly of the Charolais, Limousin and Belgian Blue. These foreign breeds have largely replaced the traditional British breeds on account of their rapid maturing and 'double-muscled' carcass which produces the premium carcass at eighteen months. However there are signs that the Aberdeen Angus may be making a comeback and certainly there is a demand sufficient for its individual identification on the supermarket shelves. This old British breed is of exceptional quality and, although slower maturing, does better on poorer quality nutrition and so is a good hill cow. However cattle are not the mainstay of the farming economy being kept in the main 'to keep the land sweet' that is, to make good manure!

The heafed sheep are still the most important part of the hill farm enterprise and the flocks are self-contained as regards the ewe lambs of

James Alderson of Stonehouse, 1930s

which three-quarters are retained and the others sold for breeding in September. Of the ram lambs about thirty of the best are retained entire for exchange at the tup sales in September; the castrates are sold for meat in their first year. There is a three-year cycle or age pattern whereby the ewes are kept on the heafs for three years after which they are sold down onto the lowlands in mid life. They have a further three years breeding in which they do exceptionally well. Foot and mouth disease disrupted this pattern to some extent in that losses of the breeding stock meant that older sheep had to be kept longer to breed on the heafs, simply to maintain the quality of the stock. Also the young sheep or hoggs that could not be moved back to the fells from their winter grazing, had lost their memory of the home heaf and would wander away if left to their own devices. Re-hefting using fencing has had some success, but has been expensive. More successful has been the 'old fashioned shepherding' such as practised by Mr Clifford Harker, whereby forty hoggs were re-introduced to their home heaf at the beginning of April 2002, were visited, fed and collected for three months on a daily basis up to the present time. This has proved particularly labour intensive and is not something that the younger generation from a different background would probably contemplate.

Sheep dogs have been, and still are, essential to shepherding. The collies are generally bred on their home farm, but a good dog is highly valued and can change hands for as much as £1000 and perhaps more. They are generally trained as pups by their owners in company with an older experienced dog with whom they serve a sort of apprenticeship. Once they would have accompanied the shepherd at heel as he rode the fells on horseback, whereas nowadays they can often be seen riding behind their master on his quad bike to their respective flocks. Sheep dog trials are a popular country pursuit and have attracted a wide following due to television. Not all dogs bred are suitable for the job but an old sheep dog that has served his time well will be eased into semi-retirement and when his time comes may be buried around the home farm to join previous generations of faithful dogs forever guarding their flocks.

Tup sales and tupping

The farming year properly begins in November when the rams, newly purchased to bring in fresh blood to a flock are 'introduced' to the ewes and tupping begins.

The ram or tup sales are held at Hawes and Kirkby Stephen at the end of September and are one of the high points of the year with much preparation of tups for sale on the home farms and friendly rivalry. Prices rise inexorably from year to year and the shortage of tups promoted by foot

Joctlynth Campbell

and mouth disease, and the desire to restore quality was no doubt instrumental in forcing the top price for a ram to £100,000 in 2002! There is an ancient custom of the seller giving the purchaser 'luck' money which is believed to have its origins in Viking tradition and continues to this day. It is debatable whether a ram's six to eight years of service can ever compensate for his purchase price but prestige is a great driving force. The sheep farmer's love and pride in the quality of his stock means that to have a really top-quality animal is something to be aimed for more than the usually recognised marks of success such as cars or houses! The tups for sale are washed, manicured and beautified to a degree only experienced by super models.

Once the rams have been bought, the business of tupping begins in earnest. The rams are 'reddled', that is marked by dye on their chests, which marks any ewe they have serviced. This dye is often red, but other colours can be used to show which ram has serviced which ewe.

From then onwards into the winter months the in-lamb ewes are retained on the home farm whilst the ewe hoggs are sent off onto the lowlands. This practice has been carried out for the past fifty years and is encouraged further by English Nature to reduce grazing on the fell. The rams are removed from the ewes by Christmas and life settles down for the winter. This is the time for jobs such as walling and, in January or February, as soon as the fields are hard enough from the winter frosts, 'muck spreading' takes place, where the manure from the midden is spread on the fields.

The turn of the year means that the ewes need extra feed and those on the fell collect by the roadside awaiting and mobbing any likely vehicle that might be bringing their rations of hay or silage, or from March onwards, sugar beet. Once it would have been 'make do'; heather and moss were the only means of sustenance and in bad winters losses were considerable. The consequence of better provision is that ewes are more likely to be carrying twins than formerly, a doubtful blessing since in the cold wet springs often one lamb is enough to rear. But the ewes usually manage, and their own losses have been considerably reduced.

Lambing

Lambing takes place from mid April onwards. The first-time ewes have their lambs under cover indoors, whereas the older, more experienced ewes lamb outdoors. Normally, few problems are encountered

Clive Owen, Ravenseat, with yow and lamb.

during the birthing process itself and losses from infections are few, although unduly severe cold, wet weather can kill young lambs. The good mothering qualities of the Swaledale ewes generally ensure that vulnerable youngsters are protected from the elements by sheltering them against the walls, and they usually survive and thrive. A lamb might have to be hand-reared if its mother dies, or, if it is one of a multiple birth, when its mother is unable to provide for all her lambs. However, after the foot and mouth epidemic ended, the need to recoup losses has meant that older ewes have been retained as breeding stock for longer than would have been normal. Subsequently, losses to these older ewes are greater than with young ewes, and means there is a higher proportion of orphan lambs - which all adds to the work load at this busy time!

Twin lambs are not uncommon and even triplets can occur, but multiple births are not sought, it being considered that one good lamb is sufficient for a hill 'yow' (ewe) to rear. The lambs grow quickly and are particularly active, practising their survival skills from an early age by running and leaping from rocks or high ground. Whoever has watched lambs at play cannot fail to recall the school playground when gangs of

Ewes and lambs on Black Howe

youngsters run and sweep around. Lambs, like all young animals, are intensely curious and adventurous, and keep their poor dams in a constant fret as to just where their naughty child has got to. There is no end to the loud and restless bleating during those first few weeks. Sometimes tragedies do occur and lambs fall into gutters, becks or rivers and don't return. Their mothers bleat forlornly for a day or so, but luckily they seem to forget and to get on with life, and do not appear to exhibit the long mourning which characterises our own species.

Tan Hill Show

By mid May, lambing has finished and the ewes with their lambs are removed onto the fell to allow the pasture to grow for cutting later in the year. Now is time for the big spring event the Tan Hill Sheep Show which is held on the last Thursday in May. This grew out of the old shepherds' meet more than fifty years ago and indeed in 2003, celebrated its fiftieth anniversary. At an informal meeting held in November 1951, a number of local farmers, the two survivors of which were at the time of writing Mr. Dick Metcalfe and Mr. Clifford Harker, agreed to inaugurate the Tan Hill Sheep Show. Mr. John Herbert Clarkson of West Stonesdale was the first secretary in 1946 and Mr. Harker was secretary from 1964

Ewe hoggs line up at Tanhill Show.

to 1989, a position now held by Raymond Calvert of Hoggarths.

The Tan Hill Show, designated The Northern Swaledale Sheep Show, is open to all members of the Swaledale Sheep Breeders' Association, and is regarded as the best show for Swaledales throughout Yorkshire and the north of England, attracting interest from as far as Derbyshire. The show generally attracts thirty to thirty-five exhibitors and is open to all types of breeder. It is the ambition of every exhibitor to produce a supreme champion - any breeder's dream!

The exhibitors are from the five districts of the association and the judges are in rotation from among the members. Classes are divided by sex, age and singles or multiples - gimmer-hoggs or tup-shearlings (see Glossary).

But, beside the serious business of showing, the event is very much a social occasion. It is much looked forward to and news and gossip are exchanged just as they always have been, despite our modern communications. On a fine day families can picnic out of doors, or can seek the comfort of the Tan Hill Inn if the weather turns bad.

Jim Alderson hand clipping at Becks' Meeting House, circa 1935.

Haymaking and shearing

During the month of June the grass is growing quickly, and the weather is watched carefully because too much rain can flatten the grass and make the cutting, and more especially the drying, very difficult. On the other hand, too dry conditions mean that the yield is reduced. In Swaledale, if the farm is in the Environmentally Sensitive Area scheme (the ESA), hay is not taken until the flower heads have seeded to ensure the survival of the wild flowers. The government Department for the Environment, Farming and Rural Affairs (DEFRA) determines the date, usually early in July, at which haymaking can begin. This date is later than that given to the farmers on the lowland pastures, and can be a source of some anxiety, because the time available for haymaking is necessarily reduced. This means that once the weather is seen to have settled and several days of relative dryness are forecast, the mowing machines are out from dawn to dusk, and are quickly followed by raking and tossing the mown grass either by hand or by machine to aid its drying. If the summer is particularly wet then silage is made instead, because the cut grass need not be dried as for hay but can be compressed into bales while still full of moisture.

No sooner has the hay been taken in than the sheep have to be

Above the Hall family packing fleeces and left, Jim Alderson hand clipping at Stonehouse.

51

Collecting hay bales ready for storage

Hay bales loaded into field barn.

A typical Swaledale hay field near Muker.

Foddering on the fell in winter.

Left, sheep dogs belonging to the Hall family and below, the Mottram brothers, mending a stretch of wall on Ashgill.

Top, Tanhill pub and show ground.

Centre, assessing form.

Left, the champions!

55

Top, Raymond Calvert showing off the paces at Tanhill Show.

Below, judging ewes at Muker Show.

Above, the judge takes a closer look at two tup lambs at Muker Show - Jonathan Hall to the left with Lisa Huddleston (née Hall). Photographer A. Pennington.

Below, Muker Show' dog class.

Above, the dairy tent at Muker Show and below, fell racers on the home stretch.

collected for shearing and dipping. They are sheared or clipped to remove the heavy wool and so allow the new fleece to grow and to aid generally in the comfort of the sheep in hot weather. Dipping removes any skin parasites. Once the sale of the fleece was an economic necessity, and older people remember when the price fetched by the wool crop paid the rent for the year, but now that individual fleece prices have dropped as low as twenty-five pence per fleece, it is no longer cost-effective.

Clipping the sheep was done formerly with hand-held shears but now is performed principally with electric shears, either by the farmer with any help he can get, or by contractors who travel from farm to farm. To hold a sheep with one hand and remove the wool as an unbroken fleece is a skilled process but can be done by an experienced operator in as little as two to three minutes. The fleeces are wrapped and sold principally for carpet making, although there has been some interest in wool as an insulation material but this is not as yet on any large scale.

Muker Show

A brief lull during August allows those who can afford the time to have a short holiday, but usually there are many jobs to be done or caught up with. However, the end of summer is marked in Swaledale by the Muker Show.

This local show is held early in September and must be one of the most enjoyable and picturesque of village shows. Like all traditional events it arose from humble beginnings - in this case from a bet between local farmers of the comparative merits of two tups! In 1893 the Swaledale Agricultural Society was formed at a meeting held in the Muker Literary Institute and the first show was held that year on 27 September. The site of the show in the pasture behind the village and at the foot of the fell must be without equal anywhere. The Swale is wide and broad in the valley-bottom having emerged from the deep ravine carved out behind Kisdon hill when the ice was melting some ten thousand years ago. The tree-lined valley gives way to the scarred fell which rises to one thousand six hundred feet above sea level and is the challenge posed to the fell runners who take part every year at the show.

As always it is the Swaledale sheep who have remained the mainstay of the meeting and classes are held for all categories of either sex which draw an attentive crowd. In addition, large marquees contain poultry, vegetables, flowers, crafts and all manner of home produce. It is a wonder and a delight that good people still make butter and cheeses as well as traditional cakes, pastries, bread and jams. To spend an afternoon at the Muker Show is to take part in a traditional event that seems timeless and may it ever remain so.

The show draws to a climax after the judging when the fell races start and the Muker Silver Band welcomes in the runners of the respective classes. How especially good it is to see young people taking part, and, in an age where we are continually castigated for not taking enough exercise, there are those who practise for such events in what must be so often arduous and inhospitable conditions. Why do we not hear more of them and others like them?

And so to the end of the year when the tups are bought and sold at Kirkby Stephen and Hawes auction marts, hopes are raised - and dashed - money is exchanged and records are set, then back home and the yearly cycle starts again.

Hoggarths

5
THE FARMERS' TALES: RECOLLECTIONS OF SEVENTY YEARS IN SWALEDALE

Mr George Calvert of Hoggarths, Keld

When I look back and see the changes that have taken place since I was a boy! I went to school in Keld and at that time there would be about thirty to thirty-two scholars, and that was up to the age of fourteen. I left school when I was fourteen and that was in 1935. Farming in those days was just about hopeless, it was very poor because of the low prices round about 1930 to 1932. You could just about make the rent and live very frugally, and hope that things might be better next year. I will never forget till my dying day a Sunday school outing we had in about 1935. We went on a coach trip to West Hartlepool from Keld, and until I saw those children I thought we were poor. I saw children on the streets without shoes, some were wearing torn trousers and no shirt, some were running barefoot. I was walking along this street and carrying a bag of sweets in my hand, and a boy ran up and snatched it off me and that was the last I saw of him. We saw the parents of some of the children. They were street musicians, playing an accordion, and they were standing in the gutter because they were not allowed to stand on the pavement. They had a cap on the pavement for people to drop money into. Further down the road was a blind ex-soldier and he was singing, just singing for a bit of brass, and he had his cap down on the pavement. When we got back on the bus to come home folk were saying, 'Farming is bad in Swaledale, but things are a lot worse in Hartlepool.'

A lot of people were leaving the land at that time, they were just walking away. The government didn't seem to care about the farmers, the 'powers that be' and the Members of Parliament seemed to be far more interested in what was going to benefit Rhodesia, South Africa and Australia. They had money invested in those countries, and as far as they were concerned the farmers could hang on and manage without help or investment, and that carried on until the war. No one took notice of us, and when the war came, and England's farming was in a very bad way, then all of a sudden everything had to change. We had to grow everything we could because the foodstuffs could not come from Rhodesia and Australia anymore.

The government then had to do everything they could to bring about a change in farming, and the farmers responded in every way they could to produce more, and do the best they could for England. Then when the war finished, they put a Labour Government in who said that never again would they let farming go back down to where it had been in the thirties. Farming prospered during the first world war because the country could not import food, but after the war finished they let farms dwindle and dwindle down and down until 1939, when the government was faced with war again. England was stuck up against it, and the farmers had to produce the necessary food and they even started to plough up here! They tried to plough up at Pry House, but it was that stony that they had to give over! But from the beginning of the war there was a different attitude towards farming. After the war there was a Labour Government, Tom Williams was the Minister for Agriculture, and he made a good job of things because everything the farmers could produce was wanted. The government said we must not let farming drop back to where it was in the thirties. If there is a third world war, which wasn't very far off at one time with Russia, the government aimed at England being as self-sufficient as possible, and they brought in subsidies to help make farming pay. Ever since t'end of the war the government has tried to make

George Calvert

farming a viable enterprise. A lot of people round here started keeping cows, and they started selling milk to the dairy, and things went well.

Now it is a very different story, and it is getting to a state where you could quite well do without any farming in England. The government can buy food by importing it, and then if you import, you export, and that is the change. We could sell agricultural machinery overseas, and buy back all the butter and cheese we need. We have here people still selling milk, but the price has been brought down to such a level it is not worth doing because they can import milk cheaper.

The government didn't ask us to increase the number of sheep we have. Swaledale sheep are very good to eat, and we sell off most of the male lambs to the meat trade, but now the wool just isn't viable. Up in Swaledale every farm has a quota or a given number that you can put on the moor and you keep to that, but you could keep more inside. The sheep round here are all Swaledales; now fifty or sixty years ago if you put a compass on Keld and drew a circle, you would draw pretty well where the Swaledale sheep are. When you go over to Wensleydale you get the Dalesbred sheep which is another flock, and then if you go to Kirkby Stephen and Ravenstonedale you get a breed called the Rough Fell. Over in the Lake District they have the Herdwick, nice little sheep, and then further up to the Tyne and Weardale you get the Scotch Blackface, and they have the Scotch Blackface sheep on the East York Moors. The reason why the Swaledale breed has become very popular is because they are used for crossing to breed fat lambs. Actually the breed has expanded out a lot at the expense of other breeds. They are very hardy, they are good mothers, and they are good to winter and all that because they can take the snow. Farmers like to cross a Swaledale ewe with those Blueface Leicester tups, they like to breed these half names, and these lambs are very, very much in demand. This has made the Swaledale sheep very popular, and they have done pretty well over these last years, but then the foot and mouth came and did us a great bit of harm.

We take our sheep off the fell in winter, and because we keep all the female lambs to breed from in their first year, they want a good winter. We send them down to the Eden Valley which is a great place for them, and we also send some to Durham. The sheep go down in November and they stay there till the end of March. The reason why the sheep were moved to winter away was because they graze on heather moors, and the powers that be, the landlords, said that they wanted the sheep off the moor and so as not to eat the heather in winter. It was not just the landlords who did not want all that heather being nibbled because of the grouse shooting, the conservationists said the heather areas were getting less, and they were concerned about some cases of over-grazing. They wanted any ground that had heather to remain like that. Just down the road from here there is a pasture that has a bit of heather in it, and no one has put any stock there, and the heather is blooming. It is now growing all over the place, so in some ways it is good for the farmer to move his stock in winter, and until the coming of the foot and mouth the job was working well.

The authorities gave all of us an incentive to send the sheep to the lowlands and bring them back here in time for lambing, and then put them back up on the moors. Early on in the winter sheep don't eat the heather because it is dead and it's unpalatable, but in autumn it gets up and blooms, and sheep will eat it then. And when there is snow on the ground sheep can absolutely massacre it. The farmers agreed we would all take the sheep off the moor, and for the first two or three years that was grand. Then in 2001 we were hit with foot and mouth.

Pry House

Mrs Jennie Harker of Pry House

My grandfather came over Tan Hill from Arkengarthdale with a horse and cart and all his belongings at the age of seventeen. He had heard that there was an untenanted farm in Upper Swaledale called Ravenseat, and he was fully aware that all the farms round here have hefted sheep that go with the farm. A stock of sheep always goes with the farm, so there was no big financial outlay to find. Eventually my grandfather married a lass from Stonehouse, a farm at the head of Swaledale, she was an Alderson, and they brought up a family of five sons and one daughter. All five sons and the girl went into farming. In the middle of the 1930s my grandma and grandpa bought a farm and moved near Keld, taking with them my aunt and the younger boys, but my father stayed on and farmed Ravenseat with another brother. Dad married in 1939, but remained at the old family farm at Ravenseat, and that is where we were all born, and all the time we were growing up there, my mother, my father, and an uncle were also living there. Then my aunt married and came to live and farm at Pry House farm, where we live today, and you could say we had a family network of three farms.

I went to school in Keld, and at that time there were twenty-six children in the dale, and there were no less than fifteen of us all from these three top farms. We used to be picked up in a school car, and my dad's youngest brother did the school run. I stayed at that school until I was fifteen years old. Some pupils went down to Reeth School for their last year, but I was the only one in my age group, so they wouldn't provide either a car or funding just for me, so I stayed at Keld School all my school life.

When I was at school, all these houses were fully occupied. They were proper farms, all making a living, and at that time Keld had a shop, a post office, two chapels, a village hall and a pub. The pub was sold when I was in my last year a school, and that was a sad day for everyone when the Cat Hole Inn was sold up.

I worked on the farm when I left school, and I always imagined I would marry a farmer, I never thought of anything else. We got married in 1962 and we lived in West Stonesdale, another stone's throw from here, and we farmed there for fifteen years. Then my uncle had a stroke, so we moved to this farm in 1977. The story of the valley is a story of contraction. As farms become vacant sometimes the farm houses have been sold off, and the land has been taken up by a neighbouring farm. But this farm has never changed and I would love to think that when we go it will stay as a farm for a young person to come into, because it's got these sheep that go with it so a young person wouldn't have to find a

Mr Clifford Harker with a Pry House ram.

Mr Jim Whitehead, son of Raper Whitehead and Jennie Harker's father,
pictured at Ravenseat.

quarter of a million pounds as they have to do nowadays. It is very hard getting a foot on the ladder for farming, and the young ones just can't get the money together.

Up till about five years ago we used to have about ten cattle, cows and calves, but this is only a small farm, and we found it wasn't worth the while financially. We used to milk them and we made cheese. This was called Swaledale cheese, which is a softer kind of cheese. I used to make one cheese everyday from about the middle of June to the end of August into September. Probably I'd make one every day or every other day, however much milk we had really, and then I used just to give them away. We tried cattle as I said, but the farmers round here make their living from sheep, and our sheep are special.

The real point about this whole story is that Swaledale sheep are pedigree sheep, and my grandfather was one of the founder members of the Swaledale Sheep Association, and I think before that they were known as Dalesbred. But that would not do for us because the Dalesbred was another breed which came from Wharfedale which is the other side of Yorkshire. This breed of sheep which we call Swaledale, was found originally in about the ten mile radius of the bit between Tan Hill to Ravenseat, round by Nateby Fell and back to Keld, and that is where the breed started. All the farmers complied and they did not interbreed their sheep with other strains, we stuck with these sheep from this small patch as you might say.

This breed of sheep has been very successful, and the reason why it is successful is because it is a very hardy animal, and a good mother. It's a wonderful, wonderful mother. I am going back a number of years now, forty or fifty years ago or longer when the sheep weren't fed very much, and they could be in poor condition after a bad winter on the fells, but these sheep of ours would always look after their lambs. Most other sheep would have lambed and just walked away, and it has to be said some Swaledales did. They were in such poor condition, their instinct was to go away in order to survive, and never mind the lamb. Swaledales have proved to be one of the best mothers in the whole sheep industry. It will stick with its lamb, and bring up its lamb at all costs. Now that doesn't apply much now because the sheep are so well fed, but even so they are still very good mothers. Farmers who keep Scotch Blackface sheep come down to the ram sales at Kirkby Stephen and buy Swaledales and go and do what we would never do to our Swaledales. We would never put any other blood in them because they are pedigree! These farmers come down and buy a tup, and then take it back and give it a run through their Blackface sheep, and one of the reasons is to try to implant this mothering instinct. Their sheep would be lambing their lambs and then leaving them, and they lacked the mothering instinct.

Male lambs are castrated, and they make good tender lamb for eating, but we always keep them up to a year because when the lamb has turned a year old it develops a much better flavour. We used to have over five hundred ewes, but we lost three hundred in the foot and mouth epidemic, and we are still way down in our numbers.

Rachel Hall foddering the sheep on heaf in winter.

Mrs Rachel Hall (nee Alderson) of Bridge End/Stone House

This valley has changed a lot since I was at school here, and perhaps the biggest change has been in the houses round about. A good many have become derelict, even in the village of Keld itself, and in fact there are not many houses in the village that are still lived in full time. There used to be a school in Keld, and I went to it of course, but it closed sometime in the early 1970s because there were not enough children in the area to keep it open. I went to secondary school in Richmond, and that took an hour travelling by bus in the morning, and an hour coming home at night.

It was not so long ago that there were two shops in Keld, and my mother was the last person to keep a shop there. They sold petrol, and people calling in would say, 'Have you got this, and have you got that?' so eventually she opened a small shop. Actually over the years there have been various shops, but they all had to close, and I think my mother's shop was the last to go, and that would be ten or fifteen years ago.

There is no doubt about it people are leaving this valley. Our oldest

71

Shearing at Stonehouse with dogs.

son, Martin is a chartered accountant, and he has been working away for three years since he left university, so he is not going to go into farming - although his farming knowledge comes in very useful when dealing with clients. Our daughter, Lisa works as a nurse, but she is very keen on farming and has married a farmer, and she loves farming; then we have two boys still at home. Our youngest boy, Benjamin is the most interested in farming, and he can actually recognise sheep, it is an inbred thing. He actually can remember which sheep had which lamb last year, he knows them, and we call him our little shepherd, but if he goes into farming it will be hard - it is a hard way of life. We would not push any of them to go into farming. We encourage them to work hard at school, but who knows what the future of farming is.

The children go to school in Gunnerside until they are eleven years old. Jonathan is fourteen now and he goes to school in Richmond, which makes a long day with the two hours of travel time, and then he has to do his homework. The school in Richmond is so far away it makes it difficult for children in this valley to join in after school activities. Now, one night a week he may want to stay behind for football practice, and another night he wants to play rugby. That does not mean we have to drive

John Hall shearing with electric clippers at Stonehouse.

Benjamin with prize gimmer hogg.

Stonehouse.

over to Richmond to collect him, but sometimes I will drive to Gunnerside to meet the late bus that gets back about 6.15pm. It means you have to think ahead and plan these things, but it is nice to stay on and play foot ball after school. There are not many children around here now, just odd ones here and there, pockets of them.

Our youngest boy, Ben, goes to school in Gunnerside, and a taxi comes for him every morning. There are only sixteen children in that school now. I think they will have to keep it open because I could not imagine sending the little five year olds to Reeth. Next year no less than five eleven year old children will be leaving, and I think there is only one five year old coming into school. That school has a head teacher who teaches the junior children, and there are two part-time teachers who take the infants class. It must be one of the best schools in Yorkshire with all the attention the children get from their teachers, and then they move from a school of sixteen to a school of 1,600 children when they go to Richmond.

I remember my grandmother. She lived in at Stonehouse until 1964, and I remember staying there when we were haytiming up there, staying the night with her. Keld was a busy little place, but I was only young and don't remember too much, but I do remember our

Benjamin rolling a fleece.

75

Methodist Chapel, there always seemed to be a lot of people coming to the chapel then. And now there are only eight of us, not eight families, just eight people. There are only a few people going to the United Reformed Church; things have altered such a lot. Our Minister, a lady actually, has about eight churches. Her husband is the Minister for the bottom end of Wensleydale, and she is Minister for Swaledale. They live in Reeth, and it does work out for them quite well.

We were once quite a thriving community, but that has all disappeared. I would think most of the children want to leave the valley when they leave school. When I look back and see the children that are the same age as our older ones, some have gone to university, come back and got jobs locally, but some have gone away and are not going to come back. Some never went to university and stayed locally and became electricians, plumbers and have taken up those kind of skills. There is a balance. I think the people growing up here probably have their heads screwed on quite well and whatever they do they know it is a hard life.

There is a Women's Institute but I don't belong to it, but actually I have just completed a computer class, but it is at Kirkby Stephen. To me it is handier going to Kirkby Stephen because I can do my shopping at the same time. For instance, yesterday morning my husband and I gathered the moor first, then I changed in the back of the Discovery, went off for my computer class, did some shopping, came back, changed again and dipped some sheep, and came home in time to be here when Ben came back from school. It is handier for me to go to Kirkby Stephen, which is in the other direction in Cumbria.

When I left school I went to work on my father's farm, and that was the expected thing to do. I married a farmer and so all my life has been farming, and I have to say there have been ups and downs.

Ravenseat Farm

Mr Clive Owen of Ravenseat

I came to this farm about fifteen years ago. We had a hill farm before, so I was used to hill farming, and I have always been very interested in breeding Swaledale sheep. Although we lived in Cumbria, we still bred the Swaledales. They have such a reputation as one of the noted breeds, and when this farm became vacant it was just such an opportunity to come here, and I decided this was the place for me, and that is how I got here. I think what is so good about these sheep is that they are so suited to these Pennine black hills. I do not know whether any other breed could live and thrive as well on this black piece of fell like the Swaledales do. It is a massive breed; it is a massive breeders' association and there is massive interest in the breed, and that makes it such a big thing to be a part of. It is our work and our hobby and everything else all rolled into one.

Since I have been farming up here I think the size of the flock has probably reduced in number. This farm is on a shooting estate, and over the years on quite a lot of these higher farms sheep numbers have actually gone down because the estate feels that with less sheep it maybe

Clive Owen and tup lamb.

benefits the heather. Also, there are fewer farms than there used to be years ago, so that would account for there being less sheep at the top of this dale than in the years gone by.

Now as you know we take our sheep off the moor in winter. That hasn't always been the tradition of course, because away back the sheep would be wintered at home, but lately it has been commonplace to move them. That is why we have the builders here at the moment because they are re-doing up some of the hogg houses. Hoggs are lambs over six months old. Years and years ago when obviously there wasn't the transport, people used to house their hoggs over winter, and in order to do that they had to make special barns which were on two levels. These barns or hogg houses had to have stone flags on both floors, because you could not have had sheep on wood because wood would rot with all the wet.

People have been taking sheep away for the worst of the winter months for quite a lot of years now, and sheep are normally a lot safer in the lowlands. For a start the weather there is much kinder, and there isn't the danger of snow and being lost in drifts, and also they probably grow bigger than they would at home.

There is talk of cutting the subsidies we get. There is a change on how the government views farming, and how they are paying us, how they are subsidising farming. It is going away from numbers and onto how the land is farmed, and in a way that probably suits these farms. We used to farm traditionally, but now we are encouraged to join in environmental schemes, and we will be subsidised for farming in a way that encourages things like wild flowers. We are fortunate in that we have never farmed intensively, and we are now getting a little reward for farming in the old traditional ways, and that is good. We are encouraged to develop the flowering meadows; if we farm the meadows without using masses of nitrogen, and don't cut for haymaking until the seeds have set, we get paid for doing that and it suits everybody. It is nice that these old meadows are protected because they had almost gone, and it is good to see the return of the old meadows to this dale again. I like to think of that somebody, some time a long time ago, who made these fields from the moor. These fields of ours have a big variety of wild flowers in late June, and all of the fields put on a bonny show. It must have been extremely hard work long long ago to have made the fields, and you wonder who built all the walls and these buildings and everything else. There was a settlement of nine houses here once, perhaps that was because of the lead

Amanda Owen, a modern shepherdess.

mines that were worked up here. I think the land we farm at Ravenseat would have had about five farms on it once upon a time, and it might have been better then, with more people and more going on. Now the only other house that is occupied up here is where the gamekeeper lives.

Hill farms have always worked with nature, possibly more so than in some modern farming practice, so in a way we are just doing what we have always done. We approve of the new government guide lines because the ministry has realised the importance of keeping a balance; on these high farms you have to work with nature, the weather and seasons rule everything.

I am not convinced about the global warming; winters certainly are not as snowy as they used to be, but they could return, we will have to wait and see. These last few winters have been very wet and we have not had the massive snow problem that we used to have. We could rely on being snowed up every year, and we still get snowed up every year, but lately the snow has not lasted. We used to be snowed up for quite a long period at a time, you could guarantee it, whereas these last few winters when the wind has been in the west we have had wet winters, weeks and weeks of it. Whether it is global warming, or whether it will all change back, we will have to wait and see. Living in such a remote farm does have its problems; we are a mile from the main road, and if it snows hard our little one will not be able to get to school when the time comes because the taxi will not get here.

We are ready for bad weather obviously, but we have to have everything safe. First we have to know where our sheep are, and then be sure our sheep are where we want them to be. We know which places are safe places, and which places are dangerous, so once we have everything the way we want it, then working in bad weather can be quite pleasant, once you are in control. Once everybody is safe, and we are certain of that, we are quite happy to wait for as long as it takes, and we never attempt to dig ourselves out. If our stock is OK and it snows hard then we get into a routine. Once we know there is a storm coming, and we hope we get warning of a storm coming, then you get your flock to safety away from the dangerous places. The sheep know where it is safe and where there is food, and where we can hand feed them, and then we get into the routine round of putting food out for them. Once the sheep are all accounted for then it is fine.

Clive feeding yows.

We still keep our older ewes up here, and only send the hoggs and gimmers down to the valley pastures, and we will continue to do that because it gives them such a grand start, they grow out so well, and we hope there will be no problem this year. I am sure all the local farmers will be sending the sheep down as usual. One of the reasons is because part of our moor is in a scheme to regenerate the heather. We cannot winter the numbers we used to years ago, and we are encouraged to join in the scheme, and it does suit us. It is not just that the lambs that winter away are much stronger and better when they return to us in the spring, but you have to remember you do not keep lambs at home for nothing. If they are here, they have to be fed, but there is always that risk, much more risk of losing them here in the open in winter. The wind and the rain is enough to wear a lot of stock down, the constant wind and rain, and you have to be pretty tough to survive. The Swaledales are tough without a doubt, but these are very hard moors, we are above 1400 feet above sea level and in those long wet spells of weather it is pretty grim out there. There is not much natural shelter, and the sheep just have to turn their bums to the wind and get on with it.

There are less sheep on the moors right now, with all the flocks that have been killed, but the sheep stay heafed, they don't move, and if there is a space they don't try and fill it. You get to know where certain sheep will be; you can rely on it that when you pop over that hill, then you will see such and such, she will be there, that is where she is. She might be driven off her patch for a bad week when she can't face the winds, but she will be back as soon as she can.

I suppose to a degree some sheep might move onto someone else's patch, but basically sheep that are heafed properly onto the land remain very loyal to it. Things or events do take them off their ground; the weather can blow them off, or grouse shooting for instance, or fox hounds, but whatever can move them off, it will only be for a short time and then they will be back again. They are shooting the grouse right now, and the sound of the guns sends the sheep scattering to the four winds, but they will come back. Give them two days quiet, and they will be back home, back to where they belong.

They tell me that the heather plant puts on a little bit of new green growth in the summer, and it is that bit of new growth that tends to be nipped out by the sheep during the winter; that means the plant fails to thrive with its new growth gone, and that is why the moors are most under threat from winter grazing. When we put our hoggs and gimmers back on the moor with their new lambs in the spring, the grasses have grown and they will eat mosses and other plants before they take a bit of heather. It is only in winter when heather comes top of their list because there is not a lot of choice then, whereas in spring heather will come bottom of their list because it is not very appetising. The grouse chicks feed on heather, and these heather moors at the top of the dale are kept in a very healthy condition because the gamekeepers are burning them on a rotation basis. If heather is not burnt it gets too old, and it gets almost woody like trees if left long enough. The gamekeepers burn the heather and that stimulates new growth which suits the grouse, and it suits the sheep.

This is a big moor for shooting, and the shooters come here on the twelfth of August, the Glorious Twelfth, and they were just out here yesterday. They don't shoot the sheep, even by mistake! It all works very well together, the shooters and the sheep can work fine together, and we have altogether six gamekeepers that live on this estate. This is a massive shooting estate of 40,000 acres, and it is owned by a Mr. Miller who has the lodge here, and he is our landlord. He is a business man, and everybody is getting on very well with him. He has not been here long, five or six years, but it is all working very well. The shooters and the farmers can all work together fine, and the young farm lads are going out grouse beating and enjoying doing it. I think a healthy moor is good for grouse and sheep and I think they have got the balance right. In other areas possibly not, because there can be conflict between shooters and farmers, but on this estate at the moment it is working well.

We have gamekeepers as I mentioned, and when you have gamekeepers you don't have foxes. We have hare hounds who come up here once a year, but we don't have fox hounds. We used to, but we no longer have a fox problem because the gamekeepers shoot them. A few years back foxhounds used to meet here at Ravenseat, and we had no problem with them other than it is not very good for spectators up here. Hunts prefer to go where sport is guaranteed. I have hunted all my life but sometimes there can be too many foxes, can't there? For hounds to work well there doesn't want to be six foxes going in different directions, there should only be one fox for the hounds to go for. We have had some grand hunts from here, but then we were unlucky with the weather a few years back and it just seemed to die off.

We have a good show of hares. I like my hares, and we have the hare hounds come, and they are called the Bleasdale Beagles. We have a grand day, not a lot of people come up to watch, and the hare hounds don't catch many hares, so I am fine with them, and it is all sport. The Bleasdale Beagle hounds have come here for quite a few years now, but they don't catch a hare every time they come, and we still have a good show of hares so I am happy for them to come. We have a lot of hares and when you drive in here late at night you will always see four or five healthy looking hares.

We don't have deer up here. If you go down the dale a bit you will find deer, but on these tops there is not enough shelter for deer. But the top farms are marvellous places for birds in summer, and I think the gamekeepers have a hand in their conservation. I think it works well that they keep the vermin numbers down - the foxes and weasels and stoats and those kind of animals are controlled, and that lets the ground nesting birds like grouse survive, and it helps other birds like curlews and lapwings and redshanks breed successfully as well. I think twenty per cent of all the curlews in England are in this dale. Whether that is true I am not sure, but that is what I was told, and when you see how tiny our moor is when you look at a map of the whole country, it is astonishing to think that twenty per cent of a species could live here!

And when you think that the whole of this dale could have been wiped out by the foot and mouth epidemic! That squiggle on the map, our dale, would have just gone. The ministry were clearing farms where there was a massive amount of stock, some farms had more stock than the four hill farmers who live up here put together. Some farmers in the Eden Valley lost everything.

It would have gone down this dale in two or three days and that would have been that. I would have started again, I would have had to begin all over again. I would have had another go I suppose because I couldn't do anything else. I do not know what they would have done with all of us, but there is a future in farming, there has to be. Ravenseat, as I say, has been famous

Raven Owen and her Welsommers.

for its stock for at least a hundred years and more, so I see it as my responsibility during my time here to keep up the same standard. I have to do my best to keep up the inheritance. I am honoured with the privilege to have Ravenseat for my time, and so I see it as my duty to keep it as good as I can for whoever comes after me.

Birkdale Tarn in winter.

6
THE SEASONS AND THE NATURAL CYCLE

Winter

In winter the treeless landscape of the high moors is hidden by snow or lashed by the heavy winter rains and life is at a low ebb. Sheep are still retained and foddered on the heafs and they gather by the roadside awaiting the arrival of the farmer in his four-wheel drive bringing them bales of hay or silage. Nowadays, the young stock are removed and sent down to lowland farms to graze richer pastures. Wild creatures appear few, but the observant eye will see occasional hares as well as the ubiquitous rabbits on winter rambles. Moles too are especially active in the winter months as they burrow their tunnels throwing up the characteristic mole hills. Although 'Moley' is familiar to generations of children from *Wind in the Willows* he is a pest up here and a constant low grade battle is waged against his incursions which can reduce whole fields to war-ravaged landscapes. Stoats make their presence known by the quick glimpse of their elegant forms with characteristic black tip to the tail - I have only seen one true ermine in which the winter fur was white except for this black tip. More generally the sad corpse of a rabbit with a fatal wound at the neck behind the head is the more usual evidence of a stoat's activity and who has not been chilled by the long shrill scream of the victim in its final long drawn out moments? But predators are not plentiful for the moors support grouse, and gamekeepers are retained to keep down foxes and other undesirables, an activity which benefits rabbits as well as grouse!

The winter silence is broken only by the occasional harsh cry of a grouse or pheasant; other moorland birds are few, and the robin and blackbird are confined to the homestead. But make no mistake, winter can be glorious too. On the occasions when snow falls and lies for a week or more the countryside is thrown into sharp relief; long icicles hang from banks and the river itself may be partially frozen over. The velvet nights are illuminated by all the stars of the Milky Way and Orion the hunter stalks the Great Bear across the cosmic wastes watched by the shy Pleides and Cassiopea. Sometimes Jupiter hangs like a great jewel in the east, or the red planet Mars and Venus herself are visible. Under particularly favourable conditions around the equinox the northern sky is illuminated by a glow having nothing to do with urban pollution, but which is from the Northern Lights that, even at these latitudes, are sometimes visible. All these sights were commonplace once but now are seen only in the depths of the countryside having been drowned out in our towns and cities by the harsh fluorescence of modernisation. We are belittled by this, our imaginations stultified and our place in the cosmos reduced to banality.

The red grouse considered by some to be our only solely British bird has long been a part of these heather moors and this game bird par excellence is protected for sport and the table. It competes with the sheep to some extent for the heather shoots on which it feeds, although this has been contested, and in recent years the sheep population has been considerably reduced on the winter fells to assist the recovery of grouse stocks which had become depleted. The birds live out on the high fells but towards autumn and winter can be seen foraging on the lower pastures, often in small family parties of an adult accompanied by six to ten younger birds. The adult red grouse, is rather a heavy bird with a cover of rich chestnut feathers, barred with bands of darker or lighter brown that provides excellent camouflage with its moorland habitat. When startled the bird emits a sharp staccato cry and flies low and fast across the heather. Grouse lay as many as ten brownish, speckled eggs in a barely scooped out hollow beneath the heather.

The black grouse, its cousin, is generally considered rather rare, but, although traditionally fond of tree cover, can be found hereabouts on Cotterby Scar, a tree covered limestone outcrop adjacent to the open fell. Otherwise black grouse have adapted to certain locations on the treeless moor at the top end of Swaledale and one of the sights of winter are these birds flying low, with their characteristic long glide, over frozen Birkdale tarn. The male black grouse or blackcock is a spectacular gentleman with a red flash on his jet-black feathering and a characteristic lyre-shaped tail. In spring courting displays known as 'lecs' can be seen when several blackcocks will display for the attention of the more undistinguished hens.

The pheasant is considered to be an introduced species but there is no doubt it has become naturalised and is a common sight in winter, even more so than the grouse, bringing a welcome flash of colour to the pastures of the dale. It lives in small flocks of both males and females, which can be seen cooperating in clearing the frost and snow from the

Firs upstream from bridge in winter.

Bridge at Stonehouse and Ashgill in winter.

frozen ground of the home pastures with beaks and claws in order to feed on the underlying shoots. The pheasant's well-marked three-toed prints with tell-tale tail feathers like an accompanying train are conspicuous over the snowy fields.

Into Spring

Spring comes late to these northern uplands. The first greening of the fields is not seen until mid-April when the flocks return to lamb on their home pastures. From then until mid-May primroses, violets and wild pansies appear on sheltered banks; coltsfoot and celandines too. By the riverside the palm, hazel and alder catkins appear and the blackthorn bursts into bloom. The tender green of new-leafed trees hold spring's advance in suspense as the days lengthen and so slowly warm. Finally bluebells show in wooded copses and June is ushered in with the blossoming of the may trees and the blooming of the wild rose on roadside and river bank.

Long before all this shy unfolding, the turn of the year is heralded by the return of the wading birds from sheltered coastal estuaries. As the days lengthen in January our eyes scan the skies, hoping for the first sightings of our visitors - and then they come at the end of the month (in 2003 they arrived on 27 January). First the lapwings come in ones and twos, then in threes and fours until one day a cloud of between thirty and forty wheels into view over the top pasture making their characteristic cry of 'pee whit, pee whit'. They come and go but by early March the lapwings reappear permanently to reclaim their territory on their ancestral pastures.

Soon afterwards the curlews arrive, making that most evocative and memorable of moorland cries, a long drawn melancholy and yet entirely tuneful piping call. After this, thick and fast, they are joined by the snipe and redshanks, both smaller and more delicately made cousins of the curlew with the same camouflaged feathering, except for the redshank who, as his name suggests, sports a pair of coral-coloured legs, reminiscent of a miniature flamingo! What all these birds have in common is that, as waders, they frequent in winter the sea shore and in summer the marshy uplands to feed on the invertebrates they dig out with their long delicate beaks. March is born in by a cacophony of sound extending well into the evening and sometimes after nightfall the moors seem truly to come alive with their music.

These birds make their nests on the ground on the high pastures and on the moorland itself. By late March it is not uncommon to come across a shallow nest composed of loosely woven grasses and containing up to four eggs. The largest eggs, belonging to the curlew, are greeny-coloured, and flecked with brown. Often the nests are hidden from view by grass drawn over them and great care is needed when stepping out over the moors in the breeding season. Be that as it may in the high pasture near Firs many birds nest and rear their young, alongside the sheep and their lambs. There doesn't seem to be conflict, although they're in such numbers that the farm road which traverses the pasture has to be crossed with care in May so as not to run over scurrying fluffy chicks that have ventured out from the nest to the consternation of their parents!

This 'nursery' pasture has little to recommend it at first sight consisting as it does of a mixture of grasses heavily threaded with rushes and the marsh marigold advertising its poor drainage. However this modest 'unimproved' pasture supports in great profusion all the waders, something upgraded land could never do and consequently, the lapwing and other wading birds have declined on the downland, richer lands.

The numbers of wading birds that frequent these northern hills during the breeding season has led to particular sites being designated Sites of Special Scientific interest or SSSI's. Additionally a European recognition of their ecological importance has been granted. These designations put restrictions on the use and management of the uplands, on the removal of peat and on the drainage to maintain them indefinitely as special sites.

Waders, however, are by no means the only birds. Down by the river an early visitor is the oyster catcher, a flamboyant bird in black and white and sporting bright red legs. The arrival of these handsome birds coincides with that of the lapwings and curlews and their loud piping cry announces the arrival of one or two breeding pairs. These soon appropriate to themselves particular sections of river bank which they patrol searching and presumably feeding on the small trout which can be found in these higher reaches of the Swale. It would seem that the oyster catcher is a fairly recent immigrant - no one quite knows why - perhaps our moorland streams support a richer diet than can be obtained from the over-fished coasts. Although they do join with the other waders in digging for food in the low lying marshes, they generally keep to the river bed by the side of which they build their stony nests and on whose banks their camouflaged offspring can occasionally be seen. The river supports other species too; at least a pair of heron can be seen winging a slow and rather graceful flight up and down the upper dale. More modestly the dipper, a small brown and white bird, patrols its designated territory of river often announcing itself quite cheerily to those who may be about to come too close.

In the early morning the ring ouzel vies with its cousin the blackbird for supremacy. The ring ouzel sports a striking white collar and sings loudly from the leafless ash tree emulating but not surpassing the blackbird. The ring ouzel is more adapted to the treeless landscape making a nest in banks or barns although our persistent and solitary pair of blackbirds has chosen the inside of a small barn, which they retain from year to year. The song thrush is occasionally seen but not consistently, although his cousins the fieldfare and mistlethrush are frequent winter visitors which descend in flocks upon the waterlogged pastures.

A diverse collection of other birds including finches, wagtails and meadow pipits can be seen and heard around the farm and pastures; of

Swaledale birds of marsh and fell - clockwise from top - blackcock, pheasant, lapwing, oyster catcher, dipper, redshank and curlew.

these of particular note is the yellow wagtail which is generally regarded as rather rare. The wren, our smallest bird is plentiful though shy; but one day in spring we were alerted by strange musical pipings that seem to fill the air, seeming to come from nowhere in particular but present everywhere. We were reminded of Caliban in Shakespeare's *The Tempest* who said, 'the isle is full of noises, sounds and sweet airs, that give delight and hurt not,' when suddenly we saw the source - a large family of fledgling wrens had just left their nest in the may tree and were filling the air with their song.

Spring is not really here until the arrival of the swallows. We wait in anticipation until, regular as clockwork on the first of May the first swallows arrive to make a reconnaissance of our barns and their habitual nesting sites. I have to remember to open the door of the large barn to let them in to take up residence among the rafters, always hoping that our well-fed cats will be too lazy to go after them! Some years too the house martins have appeared and although common lower down the dale they are more inconstant visitors here. Their carefully constructed nests of mud and hair under the eaves of the house are sometimes retained year after year and the rearing of their young can even be watched in close up from the bedroom window.

But these are not the only birds. The fells are also home to raptors or birds of prey among which can be counted the merlin, hen harrier and peregrine falcon as well as the more common buzzard. More recently upper Swaledale has been assigned a European designate for habitat protection for these birds.

Spring into Summer

Late spring and early summer sees the full blooming of the meadow and wayside flowers. The sheep are removed from the lower pastures by the end of May to graze on the fells and the meadows are allowed to grow for hay time. The meadows support a rich variety of wild flowers and some years ago the then Ministry of Agriculture Fisheries and Food (MAFF) gave the whole area an Environmentally Sensitive Area (ESA) designation, which we were invited to join. Grants to maintain traditional herb species and to offset financial losses from the introduction of more-productive grasses, enhanced by nitrogenous fertilisers, were offered by MAFF. The grants had restrictions on the time of grass cutting to allow the flowers to pollinate and the seed to set. Most people hereabouts have, for the most part, taken up these grants. I think it is no exaggeration to say that this has saved the old hay meadows from extinction in the nick of time.

The dale beyond Reeth has the 'improved' grasslands whose uniformity can be contrasted with that of the upper dale in which the old hay meadows appear in late June in their full glory. I well remember my first sight of the gold of the buttercups, the purple of the gentians, and the red of the clovers interspersed with the white of the ox-eye daisies in the fields around Muker and Thwaite spread out before me with all the semblance of an Elizabethan tapestry. These are 'the lilies of the field' of which the Bible speaks and are a part of our heritage as much as a painting by Constable or Turner and should be valued as such.

A closer examination of the composition of the hay meadows reveals different layers each characteristically bejeweled with flowers. The upper and immediately most visual layer includes bright yellow buttercups, both common meadow and creeping kind, together with slim spikes of red sorrel, clumps of white ox-eye daisies and is laced with the dainty umbellifore with the unlikely name of pig or earthnut - so called from the tasty tuber at the base of the plant! Splashes of blue-violet mark the site of meadow cranesbill and its more delicate cousin the wood cranesbill and in the moister meadows the creamy spires of meadow sweet complete the outward canopy. Deeper, forming a middle layer appear the richly coloured and fragrant red and white clover, blue bugle, and yellow bird's-foot trefoil and hayrattle, whilst deeper still are found the delicate blue flowers of the speedwell and forget-me-not, miniature florets of white eyebright, ruby-red milkwort and golden cinquefoil. On marshier ground grows pink ragged robin, marsh marigold and lady's smock with the common spotted orchid a striking presence. The margins of meadow and country roads include additionally lace-like cow parsley, creamy yarrow and purple knapweed, the wild geraniums, purple cranesbill and pink herb robert growing in the stone walls.

No less memorable than this visual feast is the olfactory sensation. The subtle perfume of wild honeysuckle and rose, overwhelmed by the heightening intensity of honeyed clover and culminating in the intoxication of a newly-mown meadow in early July, is quite without equal.

If June and early July are the bridal months of summer then late July into August must be counted as the honeymoon time in which the frothy

Winter fields from Kisdon - photographer Neil Thornton.

Peat hags near Birkdale Tarn.

Downstream from bridge near Firs.

Birkdale Tarn frozen in winter.

Above, spring time behind Keld and left, primroses on moss bank.

Below left, a lapwings' nest. and Herb Robert on a dry stone wall.

*Top left, dog roses,
above a red admiral,
left, meadow flowers
and below,
autumn maples.*

lace of meadow sweet and pink wild roses gives way to the purple and gold of summer in all her majesty. Rosebay willowherb and foxgloves flaunt their carmine spires amongst golden rod and ragwort on the field margins, whilst in mid-August rolling seas of purple heather clothe the moors. Harebells nod delicately on field banks, and lavender-fragrant purple thyme, accompanied by ever-present cinquefoil, adds richness to the higher ground. Even thistles with their purple heads held high add presence and, moreover, provide food in their seed heads at the end of summer for the charms of goldfinches which feed on them.

Such exuberant variety doesn't just happen by itself; it is the happy outcome of animals grazing on natural pastures fertilised with their manure: in short, working with nature. Grazing prevents stronger plant species from over-running the more delicate flowers and so maintains the variety. Grazing, however, must be interrupted for a period to allow the plants to grow, flower, and be pollinated to produce the seed for the following year. Making hay, rather than silage, allows for this, and for the chicks of wading birds to mature and leave their nests. In this way a wide variety is maintained contrasting with the tendency to monotony which so often characterises modern farming practices; the effects of which spread along the ecological chain diminishing plant and animal life. Thus mixed farming as practised for centuries, and still is in these parts, has contributed to and helps maintain the natural biodiversity.

For a time, mid-August is summer's fulfilment: nests are emptying and the fledglings are trying out their wings; the swallows and martins dive and sweep across the skies. Young wagtails peck at our lawn looking for grubs, while wrens treat the dry stone walls like tenement blocks. Tits and chaffinches and charms of goldfinches visit the thistle heads. On the pastures the lapwings begin to gather in large flocks of sixty or more. Oyster catchers and curlews all get ready to leave in autumn for the estuaries, their winter feeding grounds.

The fields are resting after the hay has been gathered in, and preparations for autumn are on the way. Rowan trees are filled with unripe berries, as is the rose and the sloe. On the moors the heather is a drift of purple and the air is heady with its honeyed smell. To walk through it is to release a mist of pollen and to startle any families of grouse which might have escaped the shoot.

...and so to Autumn

The berries hang heavy and luscious from the rowan forming swatches of vermilion amid already-turning leaves whilst the rose hips on the bushes by the river and roadside are no less brilliant and enticing for the birds. The rowan leaves turn slowly to flame like the sunset, and the birch trees are pure gold. The maple grove which I see from my window out does them all by incorporating both the red and gold in their painted leaves. Elder berries, droop wine-dark from stems in thickets and dark-purple sloe berries can be found in more sheltered places down the dale. Hazelnuts, acorns and shining, mahogany horse chestnuts, or 'conkers', lie in profusion on the ground where they have fallen from the over laden trees.

The damp days of September are the 'mushroom months' when clusters of succulent mushrooms spring up, apparently overnight. Some years are better than others, but field mushrooms are always to be found. They vie with the puffball, which is delicious sliced and fried with bacon, and the more common horse mushroom, not poisonous but less appetising. Some years, the highly poisonous, red and white spotted fly-agaric can be found along Cotterby Scar.

On clear nights a light frost, or sometimes, a heavy dew appears on the ground and outlines the spiders' webs that hang bejeweled between the rushes. The grass, though still lush, is losing its vivid green and is attaining a lighter, more yellowish hue. The heather has faded rapidly and the moorland green is slowly turning to russet brown, a brave bright colour in the winter sun. Families of grouse and pheasant are a common sight and so are hares at this time with their handsome gold-red coats and long springing legs darting from cover.

Butterflies appear in some profusion in cottage gardens during these transitional months, which, despite the shortening days, can be surprisingly warm. Although they may not be so plentiful nowadays, we still see the vivid colours of the red admiral, the common tortoiseshell and the painted lady together with the incomparable peacock butterfly, with its jewelled wings glowing in the sun. We like to think that the nettles which we leave to grow on the rough, uncultivated edges of our holding play their part in supporting the caterpillars of these butterflies.

In 2003 the leaves hung longer on the trees and benefited from the long, hot summer. The rich store of 'sugars' in their leaves caused them to be more brilliant than usual; a trip down the dale to Richmond, even in late October, was a colour palette of incandescent hues. Maple trees, aflame with fiery gold, competed with the silver birches, oaks, horse chestnuts and beech trees in the ancient woodlands which still persist towards Richmond. The dark, hillside conifer plantations, usually so light-absorbing and forbidding, were illuminated by golden, deciduous larches which stood like palely glowing candles amid their gloomier brethren. Slowly and reluctantly, the trees shed their leaves and by November their bare branches are exposed to the stormy skies.

November and December are grey months, waiting months of the year, hastening on to the shortest day, and the Christmas festival. But they have their own special charm; some days the dawn frost lies so thick on the ground it can be mistaken for the first snowfall; other days can be wet and stormy with gale force winds. But, often they are just grey and misty; a subdued hush hangs in the air - waiting on the shortest day, the solstice when the sun leaves the deepest valleys in permanent shadow and the frost never thaws.

7

THE FOOT AND MOUTH EPIDEMIC, 2001
PERSONAL RECOLLECTIONS FROM FARMERS IN UPPER SWALEDALE

George Calvert of Hoggarths

In 2001 we were hit with foot and mouth. Our neighbour who wintered his sheep near Carlisle and they got right into it, and he completely lost them. Ours were down in Durham and there was foot and mouth all over the place, and we got caught out. We lost just over two hundred in one place, and the farmer there lost all his two hundred and fifty cows as well. We lost our young lambs, rather good ones, and there were some good show sheep amongst them. It was about six o'clock one day when the phone rang and they said, 'It is the ministry.' My younger lad took the call, and afterwards he went out side, and he did not come back in for quite a bit. When he came back he said, 'The vets have been in, and the sheep have it, and there is no two ways about it, they have got foot and mouth. They said they will start to slaughter at 9 a.m. in the morning, all the sheep and cows will be slaughtered, and you must get your valuer down and get them valued.' We heard later that men were working on that farm, and it was said they brought the virus to that farm on their feet.

When the epidemic came to Kirby Stephen we all thought we would be the next victim, and the ministry was expecting that to happen. You could tell that. It moved on from Kirkby to Nateby, but over here it did not come. Some people thought the virus could not live on our peaty soil, but I don't think that was it. The foot and mouth moved up to Brough and up onto Stainmore, and every time we heard how the disease was spreading we expected one of these days we would get it. If the foot and mouth had got into Swaledale it would have just wiped the dale out and I think that if that had happened farming up here was done for. I told my lads that. The first flock of sheep in Swaledale nearest to the infected area belongs to Jim Alderson, then the next belongs to Pry House, and the next one down the valley is our farm. This is such a narrow dale, it would have come down the valley like the west wind; it would have spread and wiped the dale out. If that had happened then all the farms would have been devastated. Our sheep are all hefted, they are localised, and if they had all gone it would have been impossible to heft any others. If you brought some sheep from anywhere else and put them out on the moor they would wander off and they could end up in Kirkby or even Tan Hill! They would just go all over the place, and it is just about impossible to heft sheep that weren't born on the moor. If the foot and mouth had come right down Swaledale it would have knocked out our best stock, and it is not too much of an exaggeration to say the whole breed could have gone. These farms are no good without their stock of sheep. You can't make a living working with cattle. This is sheep country, and we need our Swaledale breed of sheep to make our living.

We got in touch with our landlords to tell them what was happening. They live in Surrey, and they own three farms up here. The landlords kept writing and telephoning us to find out if we were alright. This farm belongs to two young ladies who inherited it down through the ages and it has sentimental value to them. They come once or twice a year to Stone House, which is their country house, and when the foot and mouth disease was spreading everywhere, they would give us a ring, 'How are you faring, are you still there?'

We were doing everything we could to avoid getting foot and mouth. My elder lad stayed in his caravan near Durham and minded those ewes at lambing time, and the younger lad took care of things at home. Everybody was thinking that it was like getting 'flu, but when the 'flu is about you hope you don't catch it but you are nearly sure you will get it in the end. With this epidemic we thought there is nowt we can do about it. We kept everything disinfected, and took every precaution we could, and of course we did not go and visit people in the danger area. I do not know whether the virus is airborne or not, but I think birds can carry it. When there is an outbreak and they slaughter all the stock, they leave the slaughtered animals on the ground for a few days, and very soon the birds are in the air on top of the carcasses. If they have been pecking about among the heap of slaughtered stock and then fly off to the next farm they can possibly infect that one. I think the wind can carry it and the birds also can.

Every farmer now and again, has an invasion of rats, and you can put poison down to get rid of them, but it would not surprise me if rats were not around when they were slaughtering the stock. Rats could spread the infection, they would just clear off in the middle of the night and go onto another farm and then they stay hidden

They had this very big market in Longtown just at the start of the trouble, and a farmer put some infected sheep in hoping for a sale, but the farmer did not know they were infected, nor did the auctioneer. These sheep came from Hexham, they were sold in Longtown and they were bought by a dealer down in Devon, and they said Devon was just about devastated. The sale in Longtown that day in February last year was like a time bomb.

Our other sheep should have come back at the end of March but we couldn't bring them back. They had to stay where they were, and lambing time came. My elder lad went down to Durham and lived in a caravan, and he had to lamb them on the farm that had them. He was very fortunate that he was allowed to go down and he had to mind what he was doing. Then shearing time came, and he had to go again and shear them down there. The government said they could not be moved, and when they came back here in the early winter, they had been away over a year. They were all costing us so much per head per week. The farm that had taken our sheep for wintering wanted them cleared off the land because they wanted their land for other crops.

It has cost us a lot of money, and now we are having to breed up from what is left of our flock. Now the sheep are back on the moor, and they have remembered it. Some of the sheep hadn't been back onto the moor for a year and a half, but when we took them back they stayed. Every farm around these fells has a certain block of moorland, and, and over the years the farms have kept to that area, and a neighbouring farm has the next bit of moor, and so on. There is a bit of intermingling at the edges, but when a ewe has a lamb in the spring, when she goes back to the moor, she will go back to that little place on the moor that she knows, even if she has been away a long time. She will go back to it with her lamb, and it will get to know that place, and so it carries on. The older ewe will heft the lamb, and then when she lambs again, she will heft again, and so it goes on. We keep all the ewe lambs, and they lamb as yearlings. We have three crops of lambs from each ewe, and then at four years old they are sold off, and that is part of our income. We may have as many as two hundred sheep for sale, and some will be going off to cross with these other breeds, like the Leicester tups to make these half-breeds. When we have had three lots of lambs from our ewes, they sometimes go to a farmer down in the Eden valley who might buy a hundred ewes from us, and buy some tups and lamb them down there, hoping to get two or three more crops off them, and by then they will be about done. They can live till about ten years old, but they are at their best at about three, four or five years old. We are sheep breeders and our income comes from selling for cross breeding, or selling the older ewes on. But this year everyone has lost a lot of money.

We will recover, there is no doubt about that, and there is still a pretty good sale for our breed; in fact you could call it a seller's market. I think in two years time when everyone has got stocked up again, prices will come down to the old level. If our fat lambs get to be too dear for the meat trade, they will start to buy in lamb from Argentine or Australia. It is the supermarkets that call the tune, and even if there is a glut of lamb their prices don't come down

I am still not sure about vaccination, I think there still needs to be much more scientific work to be done on that question. Things will get back to normal eventually, and my sons do see a future in farming; they are both good at it, it is a job they like to do, and they certainly do not want to be just workmen. We have good stock, and that is the secret of our success.

ST. JAMES'S PALACE
LONDON SW1A 1BS

From: The Assistant Private Secretary to HRH The Prince of Wales

18th June 2001

Dear Mrs Hamer,

The Prince of Wales has asked me to thank you most warmly for your letter of 11th June. His Royal Highness feels deeply for you and all those in the Dales who are suffering so much because of the scourge of Foot and Mouth. He knows that he can barely begin to imagine the horrors which you have experienced. Losing the Swaledales over-wintering in Cumbria must have been a terrible blow, but should it strike your flock at home too that would be almost unbearable.

His Royal Highness has a special affection for the Dales and he finds it hard to contemplate that glorious and unique landscape without the sheep which play a part in making it so precious. He has asked me to say that you are much in his thoughts and prayers at this desperately difficult time and he will continue to do what he can to help.

Yours sincerely,

Catriona Sutherland-Hall

Miss Elizabeth Buchanan

Mrs Jennie Harker

Jennie and Clifford Harker of Pry House

When we first heard of the outbreak of foot and mouth disease in February 2001, we thought we would be safe up here. We never thought it would spread like it did. It was worrying for those that had got it, and we knew it was an awful disease, but we were confident that up here we would all be alright. And then it got to Hawes quite early in March, and nobody ever knew how that got there, and they never have known. At first the disease seemed to be contained because the ministry was ruthless with the culling, but in some areas it spread like a fire. The disease was in lower Swaledale, and in Wensleydale a little bit, and then in Cumbria. Our sheep were wintering at Brampton near Carlisle, a place owned by one of the Howards from Castle Howard. There is a lot of land with this castle, and seven or eight years ago when we were looking for somewhere for some of our sheep to go and winter, a friend told us about this land and we started sending them there. Their land suited our sheep.

We had just over three hundred sheep away that winter, and two hundred ewes left at home. Originally we didn't really want our sheep to go away for the winter, but it was English Nature that had the idea that we should let the sheep go. The reason behind their plan was that it would be good for both the grouse on the moors and the heather if the sheep were away. It was for the grouse that the sheep were removed from one section of the moor. These organisations put quite a lot of pressure on us, and bit by bit they managed to persuade us about the benefits, and we have now wintered the sheep there for the past seven or eight years. And actually it worked well because English Nature paid for the cost of sending them, and the cost of transporting them back home. The plan last year was that the sheep would return to us in the middle of March, as they always have done, and then two or three weeks later, we would be into lambing. But by the time March came, we knew we couldn't bring them home, because no sheep were allowed to be moved anywhere. We were not allowed to even go and see them, and we daren't even try to go. Philip Howard told us he would let his gamekeeper go round to see them everyday. We had a friend there who had been keeping an eye on our sheep for us, but as this friend had sheep of his own he couldn't go near. It got to the middle of April and they were due to start lambing, and I just cried and cried. All I could think about was those poor sheep who were lambing, and no one was there to give them any attention; and suddenly there they were having to lamb all by themselves. It was absolutely awful!

They did lamb. They lambed from the 14th of April and they lambed for two weeks. The gamekeeper was going round twice a day, and we phoned him and said to him, 'Just make sure nothing suffers. Please go round them and don't let anything suffer.' The gamekeeper told us there were some really wonderful lambs, and the sheep, he said, were looking really good.

On the 25th April I had a phone call - 'Foot and Mouth Centre, Carlisle' at the other end of the phone. My heart was pounding, and I just shook all over. I saw my reflection in the mirror above the telephone and I was as white as a sheet - it was just awful, awful news. And yet we knew it was inevitable, we knew we couldn't survive. We could not see how it would ever leave us alone, but of course there was no foot and mouth disease really round this castle, it was just the three kilometre cull that was so terrible. Our sheep were in this parkland round this castle and I feel sure that they would never, ever have got it. We were never given to believe we could appeal, we were told the sheep had to be slaughtered, and that was that, no ifs or buts, but the people that did appeal survived. We were given neither time to consider nor any information stating that one was allowed to appeal. I was absolutely devastated. I cried and cried. A fortnight later the sheep we had kept back lambed, and we had a few twins, and I would go down when I had finished in the morning just to see them, and without fail I came back up the road in tears, I could not stop. I was thinking about those that had gone, thinking about them lambing and wishing I could have seen them. Even now when I think about the death of those ewes I can weep

They got culled on 28 April. They were actually due to be shot the day before, but that horrible minister was going to make a statement in the Commons on the progress of foot and mouth disease; it was all planned that these lorries would go and get our sheep on the Thursday morning, but everything was stopped until the minister had made his announcement. The lorries with our sheep on board had to stand still in case he was going to change his policy. When the minister did speak, his message was only relevant to cattle and had nothing to do with sheep at all, and the speech, as far as we were concerned, was a non event. The lorries had to re-organise themselves, and we found out eventually that our sheep were not slaughtered for two more days. We had to go through the ordeal twice, because we were informed at first that the slaughter was to be on Thursday, but we were told later it took place on the Saturday.

We also lost about fifty young sheep near Wigton in Cumbria on 1st April. They were the previous year's lambs, and that was bad enough, but it was not as devastating as the loss of those ewes. In fact we thought when we lost the young ones, that if that is the worst thing that is going to happen to us, so be it, but that was quickly followed by the slaughter of three hundred of our prize ewes. After April has passed we thought we would survive, and we would just have to start again to breed up from our remaining stock. Then, on the 1st July, we heard that the plague had reached Nateby which is only the other side of our moor, and we were under great threat again. That really, really frightened us.

I felt very angry, very frightened and upset, and I wanted to get hold of some of these politicians and just tell them what I thought. We were feeling totally up against some big monster that was just overtaking us, and we did not know where to turn. We stayed put hardly daring to breathe and just hoped it would go away, but the worry was dreadful. The road over the moor to Kirkby Stephen was blocked the day they were doing all the culling and killing in Nateby, and that day they carried out a large slaughter of sheep and cattle. The road over the moor was blocked for nearly a week. The authorities closed the road, but they didn't make a very good job of it, so we made a better job; we stuck a trailer across the road. The police didn't seem to mind and said that the trailer can stay as long as nobody objects or complains. As far as we were concerned the roadblock could remain indefinitely; we felt just a little bit more comfortable with the fact that no traffic could pass down our road, as nothing could drive over the moor. But that situation didn't last long before someone complained to the police.

We felt we had to do something because we felt so helpless. We had a meeting here and agreed to write letters to the politicians. A neighbour said to me, 'Write to Prince Charles!' I said, 'No, I can't do that,' and this person said, 'Oh yes, you can!' We knew that Prince Charles was associated with the Swaledale Sheep Breeders' Association, and he knows the breed fairly well. But the real reason we wrote to him is because he is just so sympathetic to the special difficulties in these sorts of areas. He is one who understands. There are not many people who do understand how we work, but we really honestly believe he does.

Just over a week after we had written to Prince Charles he wrote back, and it was a wonderful letter (see page 106). He did not say that we could vaccinate our sheep against foot and mouth disease or offer us any protection, but he was really sympathetic. He said he was really feeling for what we were going through, and if at any time he thought there was anything he could do, he would do it.

We were feeling so very threatened because the plague had reached Nateby. We never really worried about the outbreak in Hawes that had occurred in March, we didn't feel threatened by the one in Hawes even though it was bad, it was awful, but not dreaded because it was not on our fell. Everything seemed out of control by the time the infection reached Nateby, and I do not think the men from the ministry knew what they were doing. The plague was spreading up the road towards us, but the authorities were chasing it, they weren't ahead of it, or even with it, they were chasing it!

Nobody really knows if the plague is blown by the wind, and nobody really knows if it is carried by foxes. Some local farmers thought badgers could carry the infection. Several farms adjacent to the old railway line got it in succession, and we did just wonder about badgers. There was also concern in some quarters that deer may be responsible for the infection, but there are not a lot of deer round here. The disease was rampant round Kirkby Stephen and in the upper Eden valley, but I do not think anyone really understands the reason why it spread so quickly.

There is nobody you can really blame, but there was a lot of carelessness. There was carelessness on MAFF's part: farmers also got blamed for spreading it, and probably one or two did, but we think MAFF spread it more. We have a friend in Settle and he has an awful story to tell about how he got the plague. This farmer has his farmhouse way down a track, and he never thought he would get infected. Then one day two lorries, laden with dead carcasses came and parked on the roadside by his entrance, just near his milk cows, which were in the pasture. It was in the middle of the morning when these cows suddenly all turned and came down to the house, terrified, galloping, bawling and our friend wondered whatever had happened. When he saw these two lorries laden with dead stock he was convinced that that was the reason why eight days later his cows all went down with foot and mouth. He was on the telephone to MAFF but of course they denied the lorries could carry infection. In this case, there could be no proof, but why did the cows stampede? They literally stampeded.

We have heard other stories of how the men from MAFF broke pad-locks to get down lanes, and then the farms nearby became infected. The men were not even following their own guidelines! There is a farmer we know who lives near Kirkby Stephen who was having his sheep moni-tored because of the out break of foot and mouth disease near him, and the MAFF men came with rails to make pens to help the monitoring process. The son of the farmer, a man of about thirty, asked the men from MAFF to stop work immediately because the railings were dirty. The rails were covered with blood and dirt from the previous time they had been used, and sure enough these sheep all became infected. Foot and mouth disease is extremely infectious.

The vets themselves could have been spreading the germs because they weren't wearing masks, and it is a well-known fact that a vet who has to look inside a cow's mouth, can carry the virus in his nostrils for thirty-six hours. People round here wouldn't let the MAFF vets come onto their farms to do any testing. I said to the people in Carlisle, 'You are not coming here, we are not having you here, and if we have to have testing done we will use our own vet, but we won't allow your vet to come onto our farm.' The lady in Carlisle said, 'Calm down! Calm down! You can have your own vet!' We did have our own vet of course, and one vet from the ministry did come, he was an Irish lad and I think he was OK. They simply could not cope with all the blood testing that had to be done in this particular area.

They did not take semen from our sheep to store for the future, which they could have done. They took semen from the Herdwick sheep in Cumbria because once foot and mouth had reached the Duddon valley, everyone thought the plague would sweep right over the Lakeland fells and the breed would be lost. But on the other hand the Herdwick breed is small in numbers, and the Swaledale breed is now quite widespread.

July 2001 was horrific. Every day we spent looking at our remaining sheep and wondering if they were infected. Nateby had been totally wiped out by that stage, no sheep or cattle had survived, and then in August the men from MAFF returned to do another sweep of the fell to test all our sheep, but those tests proved to be negative. One or two peo-ple said to us they thought we would now be all right, the disease would not come up the hill from Nateby, over the moor, and down to our farm. 'It'll not come back here!' they said. This gave us some hope, but we were not convinced because, to be perfectly honest, we could not believe anything anybody was telling us, and that was the whole trouble. The worst time of all was when you felt you couldn't get to the truth, you couldn't get the truth from the politicians, the MAFF centres, and even from the vets, and that made everything very difficult indeed.

Now we are a few years on, and of course we are down on numbers. We won't ever get back because time is running out, and we should be thinking of retiring. It is time for us to retire, but we feel now that if we stay well and healthy, we will stay and try to get these numbers back, and hope we can pass on a viable farm to a younger person.

We need five hundred sheep to make this farm viable, but some of that number are our own sheep, and some go with the farm. If we stay to get back to where we were it will take us twenty years. It wouldn't take twenty years to get the numbers back, but it will take twenty years to get back the quality of what we have lost. We lost the two best hefts. We had four different hefted flocks, but the two best were taken out and slaughtered.

We love the Lake District, I just love going there and seeing those Herdwick sheep, but this is Swaledale and it is very precious. The dale is only twenty miles long, but this is where these sheep originated, and I really felt at the time that all that my grandad had done was going to be lost. I just wondered what would my grandad or dad would have said if they knew what was going on now. I don't think they would have believed it.

As for the future, that is difficult to imagine. What I think is the worst part is there is no guidance from the government at all. Always in years past there was a bit of an inkling on what they wanted the farmers to do: they wanted more meat, or more milk, or whatever, but now there is no guidance at all except on environmental matters which everybody agrees with. But it can't be solely environmental concerns, it has to be farming alongside, and the ministry does not seem to have any clear ideas on that question.

I am not even sure if there will be any farming here in twenty years time. There will have to be a lot of changes to encourage young people to farm these parts. There will be people living here because many do want to stay on here, but the ministry is geared to the environmental side and it will be a miracle if they find a good balance. They will pay environmental money but they will pay the minimum, they will pay the least they can get away with, and it will be just enough to keep people here, but it won't encourage people who have left the valley to come back. We need young people to really want to be hill farmers. The son of one of our local farmers is the sort of lad who quite likes farming, but we've heard he is leaving it. He is going on a four year course to college, and he is in his twenties now. He has had a taste of farming, he feels he has had a go, but he is not liking what he sees. There has to be more encouragement.

The environmentalists pay the money and they want a big say in what we have to do, and they rather treat us as if we don't know what we are talking about. They all have their degrees, and they have studied hard at university, and they probably know more than we do, but they don't understand!

Spring Tide

Two out of four
Rode from the north and west
Black horse and pale
Came to the valley.

Strong men wept, while
Women set their shoulders
And endured.
Children watched
Silent; powerless.

The spring was silenced.

Now, at last, a rising tide
Flows from the east.
Inexorable
Immutable
Surging westwards
Borne on the cries of new lambs.

Flooding into every field
Every fold, every cranny,
Touching everywhere,
Missing nowhere.
Gathering speed,
Racing to break,
Surf crashing joyously
Against the far fells.

A great wave, noisy
With new life.
A new spring.
A new beginning.

Vivienne Metcalf,
Easter 2002

Rachel and John Hall of Stonehouse

The spring of 2001, when we were fighting foot and mouth, we lost one hundred and eighty-five ewes and their lambs. We had sent our sheep down to near Penrith for the winter, and all seemed well at first. We were watching it all on the television, and we were hearing about this farmer and that farmer and how helpless they all felt. The foot and mouth seemed to come near to Penrith, and then it went away again, and then it came back all of a sudden, and we didn't know anything about it until we got a phone call from the man who had taken our sheep in, a relative, and he said that the next door neighbour had foot and mouth, and all our sheep would have to go. It was a horrible shock because it just seemed as though it had gone away from that area, and then all of a sudden it was back again.

These ewes that were wintering away had been lambing for about ten days, some of the lambs were very new, and some sheep hadn't lambed yet. The date was the 3rd of May, and the whole lot were slaughtered. We now know they had not got foot and mouth, there was nothing wrong with them. They were taken because they were contiguous and were within the three kilometre cull. We could not go down and see them because that would not have been safe. Our relative was lambing them for us, because we could not have gone between the sheep we kept here, and the sheep near Penrith. Normally the sheep would have come back home in March, and would have lambed on the inside land, but during foot and mouth no sheep could be moved so they all had to stay on longer. The farmer looking after our sheep was terribly disappointed, he had done a good job, he did his best, and we lost all our best ewes.

We had kept a few older ewes up here, and we also had a lot of hoggs, year-old females, and they were actually in Cumbria as well, about six miles from where the ewes we lost were grazing. At that time foot and mouth hadn't got near to where the hoggs were, but then it was their turn next because the disease was spreading. DEFRA rang up late one afternoon and said, 'We're coming to slaughter your sheep in the morning.' I was taken aback, I said, 'You will NOT. You do not have our permission!' We had lost enough, and if we had lost all those young ones, we would not have had a flock to start again with. We got in touch with a solicitor and he faxed a letter to DEFRA stating that they did not have our permission to carry out the slaughter. If we had not put up this fight with DEFRA all our young sheep would have been wiped out. They would have you believe that you cannot fight their decisions, but in the fortnight between losing our ewes and the threat of losing our hoggs we got some information. In fact, it came the day before we had that dreadful phone call; I had been listening to Radio Cumbria; it was only by chance I had the radio tuned on to that station as I never listen to it in the Yorkshire Dales, and I heard this important information, and I wrote down the phone numbers. I rang up Susannah Greenhill who comes from West Cumbria, and she was fighting for the survival of the hefted flocks. She sent information with telephone numbers of solicitors who were willing to put up a good argument to keep these hefted sheep. If we had lost the hefted flocks, we would not have been able to train any more to go on that piece of mountain. You cannot put any other sheep on a mountain-side because they would just walk off.

We had a relative who lived nearby these sheep and they had actually been looking at them. They weren't farmers, they were looking after the hoggs for us, and this relative wrote to DEFRA to verify what safety pre-cautions, and disinfectant procedures they were doing. Lady Lowther who actually owned the land that the sheep were on got in touch with DEFRA as well to confirm what disinfectant procedures they were using, and all the other bio-security measures that were being undertaken. Lady Lowther also confirmed that there were no other sheep actually round ours, so there was no risk to other animals. So after all that, it was agreed that the sheep be put under surveillance, and the vet came every day, then every two days, then every four days, and then they were blood-tested - it was a nightmare! You have just got to be resilient, you know, and everyday was a bonus. Sometimes all of a sudden the vet would ring and say, 'They had a sort of infection between the toes but I do not think it is foot and mouth.' I do have to say that the vets on the ground were very good, very helpful, and that was encouraging, but we could have lost all our one-year old lambs.

These sheep came back to us in March 2002. We could have got them back in January, because that was when they were allowed to cross the county border. DEFRA did not give us permission to move our sheep until then, even though foot and mouth finished about September 2001. When they came back they did not know where they were, and this year they have wandered a bit. They left our moor when they were six months old in November 2000, and came back in March 2002. This year we have noticed that when we put them back on the hill, after they had lambed, they moved away a lot further than normal. They have been moving westwards towards Cumbria!

In normal times sheep do not take over the land of another farmer's hefted flock, they don't move away from their own patch, but this movement has happened now because whole flocks have gone. I mean they would move a little bit, they do cross a little bit onto another flock's heft, but now when whole flocks have gone, the sheep move much more. We had a job gathering all the sheep in this year because many of the sheep have moved near to the Cumbrian border. There were such a lot of sheep culled in Cumbria, and that has left so much space. Our neighbours, the Harkers, the Owens, and the Calverts all lost sheep, and now there is so much space for them it is a job keeping an eye on them all. Our shearlings have lambed. We got licences to take tups to them, but they had to be Cumbrian tups, they had to be tups from within Cumbria because of the cross-border restrictions, so when they returned to us in March this year they were well in lamb. A lot of them had twins and it seemed nature's way of replenishing the lost stock. We got a very good crop of lambs off them.

I know they are talking about a new regulation on vaccinating to prevent the spread of foot and mouth and that question is a difficult one. We thought about it when the foot and mouth was going, and it is a question of whether you vaccinate all sheep and cows to keep them alive, or whether you ring vaccinate and kill the ones within the ring. Do you vaccinate them all like children are vaccinated, or will there be a choice? It is a difficult one, and I do not think the government handled the epidemic the best way. It got out of control so quickly, and then the so-called experts couldn't come to any conclusions. I think the vets were divided, and I do not know the pros and cons about it all. It would be a job getting them all vaccinated wouldn't it?

I think the government is not trying hard enough to keep the virus out of the country and to stop it all happening again. They ought to go to all the ports to see the sort of meat that is being imported illegally, and that is probably how the epidemic started in the first place. It could be from a sandwich from a plane, or from carcasses. There is such a lot of meat going through in all those vast containers, and there does not seem to be any regulation to stop it. We have all these regulations so that we can hardly move, but the government has not gone back to the source, they have not tried to nip it in the bud, and infected meat can easily come into the country again - it comes in from all over the place, for instance, Argentina, or the Far East. So many places are rife with it!

But here the regulations are just getting out of hand. We had enough before the outbreak, but now there are more. I filled in all the forms relating to foot and mouth, and John does the rest. There is no doubt DEFRA is getting harder to please. The person on the other end of the telephone is usually very pleasant, but they do not understand.

Round here some people that were trying to make a living out of bed and breakfast had a hard time during the epidemic and quite a few really did suffer. Those people that let holiday cottages were also badly hit. The farmers did get some compensation from DEFRA for the loss of their sheep, but the bed and breakfast and holiday homes people got nothing. There is a lady who lives right up here, right away up on the tops, and I get so many people call and ask me the way to her house, and of course last year she had no visitors. She lives way out across the fields, and there was just nothing for her because her house was so far out, and people were not allowed to walk through the field to get to her house. She had a very bad time, but things have been better since then. Someone said recently that they did not feel it was back to where it was in 2000, but certainly it has been a lot better.

When I said we got some compensation I am not sure if it was adequate. It depends how you look at it. It looked a good lump sum, but when you think those sheep were gone for good, and obviously their lambs were gone for good... you know there are two sides to the question. You got compensated for that sheep, but those sheep we lost would not have been sold for probably another three years, so you would have had the progeny, at least another two years of lambing, so I am not sure if the compensation was enough.

I sometimes wonder if there is a future in farming, but I would not want our children to go into farming unless they really wanted to, and I would say that for always, not just for now. I think a lot of people make a mess of farming if they are not totally committed to it. I think they've got to really want to do it and to have it in them, and I don't think it would be a good idea to encourage someone into farming that was not sure. We would encourage any of our children, but we would not push them.

A Dialogue

Sheep.
Where are the sheep?
The sheep
They are gone.
Gone! Where are they gone?
Up in the smoke.
Under the sod.
Let us weep.
Weep for the sheep
That are gone.

Why? Why are they gone?
Who can say.
It was said they might spread a disease.
Not a fatal disease,
But fatal to profits, to prices, to business.
So the sheep, sturdy, woolly,
Black kneed, slitty eyed,
Are killed, burned and buried?

Yes!
The sheep,
They are lost,
Lost in statistics, indecision and greed.
Let us ponder then,
And weep for the innocent sheep,
That are gone.
Let us weep!

Elizabeth Sutherland.

Clive and Amanda Owen of Ravenseat

In 2001, we had a dreadful time. In fact we had three flocks that were affected by foot and mouth. We had some sheep at Longtown, which was where it all started, on a little farm at Longtown. It was just outside Carlisle, where they hold the Longtown market, where it all went wrong, and the big disease spread came from the auction mart there, and that was not a good place to be. So we lost all those sheep. Then we had some in southern Scotland on a farm just above Gretna, and they decided to slaughter all those sheep regardless whether they had the disease or not, so we lost those. We were left with eighty on a farm at Catterick. I thought those would be safe, because they were in two fields each side of the village. There was an outbreak of foot and mouth there, so they took half of them that were on one side of the A1. So out of all our sheep we lost about five hundred altogether.

My wife was having a baby at the time we lost our sheep. She was having a home delivery, and it all went badly wrong, and she ended up in an ambulance speeding to Northallerton. The day after the birth one of the nurses came in and said to her, 'Isn't it terrible about this foot and mouth outbreak!' This nurse, who came from Catterick, went on to talk about the sheep that were being slaughtered in the field next door to her, and as she chatted on, my wife realised that it was our sheep that were being killed!

We had kept some sheep up here at home, but we lost two generations; we lost all our hoggs and all our gimmer ewes, and we had to start again. We kept some on the moor, and when you've got the mothers, you can reproduce them. We thought if we can keep the breed going, that was all that really mattered. We had to keep the blood line going, and we could reproduce from the older ewes. It will take time to recover but as long as the Ravenseat blood has been preserved that is what counts. I do not know how many years this blood line has been going, maybe a hundred years of breeding and more, and if you lost that you would never be able to replace it what ever you did. So we were delighted that we managed to keep some sheep up here. That means we are not running with all the sheep we used to do, and we are not selling sheep yet. We will recover, but we think it will take us about four years to get back to our regular pattern of ages.

What we normally do is to keep the sheep in their age group, and when they get to a certain age we sell an age group, and a younger age group comes in at the other end. The older ones get sold, and the younger ones take their place, and that goes on for ever, as it has done for goodness knows how many years.

There was one point in the epidemic when they were slaughtering right up to our boundary, they came to our moor wire, right to the fence. I thought any minute now we will be next, and I thought at one time we would be wiped out. I did everything I could, and I gathered all our sheep and put them as far away from trouble as I possibly could. I was prepared to make a stand if they wanted to slaughter my remaining sheep. I was prepared to try and plead our case to keep them if it was at all possible, but it didn't come to that.

We wondered if we could just ring up DEFRA and say, 'Keep off, keep away!' We were all very worried when the ministry eventually did get in contact with all of us because they wanted to blood test our sheep. We had a meeting, all of us, and we were not happy about them coming. They came and met us in the village hall, and we had them on our terms. We wanted our own vets to be involved because we did not want ministry people to visit the farms. We needed assurances that their men had not been to a 'dirty' farm one day, and then come onto ours the next. In some cases they were using their own sheep pens and this sort of thing, and we didn't want them to come near us because we needed to be absolutely sure that they were not coming straight off infected farms. They could have contaminated all of us.

Eventually they persuaded us, and we felt we dare let them come. We wanted to refuse, but we knew the sheep had to be blood tested, but we did not want cross infection to be our downfall. We had come so far, we had all lost sheep, and we did not want a silly mistake that they could make cause the downfall. Three of the farmers from here, Clifford Harker, Raymond Calvert and me, decided to block the road where it comes over the moor from Kirby Stephen in Cumbria, because we did not want people driving over in their cars. But they would not let us so came and took away our barricades! I do not know who actually dismantled the road block but I would think it would be the county council. We had blocked the road with trailers and stones and anything to hand, but they came and removed everything. But we thought at the time, and we were deadly serious, we did not want traffic coming over from

Cumbria because we thought the virus could be on the car wheels. If the virus had spread up here that would have killed some of the moor where there are no fences or anything. We were all sweating I can tell you!

At one point we thought, 'Fantastic, let's vaccinate all the sheep and that will be that' we really did. That was probably before we really knew much about vaccination, but our first reaction was to get it done. I think when we learned more about the possible consequences we began to have doubts. The talk was that possibly if they had vaccinated all the sheep in Cumbria this could have left sheep or stock with a sort of stigma. But at the height of things and when the pressure was on us all I do not think any one of us would have hesitated to vaccinate. If the foot and mouth were to break out again I think the general view seems to be that vaccination has a place, and the whole country should be done. Killing on a massive scale is not the answer. The sheep we lost in southern Scotland were healthy sheep. We pleaded, we appealed, we got hold of solicitors and we did everything we could to save them. The farm they were on remains fine to this day, and they never got foot and mouth. The people on the farm were very happy to keep our sheep for us, there was not a problem, but the ministry insisted on killing ours. They killed many thousands of sheep that were totally healthy.

This may sound horrible but commercial sheep can be replaced, you can just go out and buy more sheep, but these hill farms, these top farms round here, they just cannot be replaced, these blood lines cannot be replaced. I think the ministry should have considered very carefully the consequences of their action. They killed on farms in Cumbria that they should not have done, and they should have realised just what they were doing. In many cases they made a big mistake

It is a hard life being a hill farmer; we haven't much margin. We are dependent on the weather and dependent on the markets and hill farming hasn't been good. It is hard to say if it is worse now than when I started farming because you cannot get a true picture because of the turmoil following foot and mouth. It possibly puts a false value on stock and there are so many farmers trying to re-stock, so there are more people in the market place than normal. I think it will take a year or two for it all to settle down and see what the true values are going to be. But things are better right now.

Vaccination would have helped control epidemic, Penrith meeting told

THE use of "ring vaccination" around foot and mouth outbreaks, combined with the slaughter of infected animals, would have controlled the disease epidemic in Britain, a meeting at Penrith heard on Sunday.

The assertion was made by Professor Fred Brown, who was said to be a leading authority on the foot and mouth virus, during a speech he made to an audience of more than 250 people, many of them farmers, who crowded into the Hired Lad meeting room.

According to Prof. Brown, vaccination was used successfully in continental Europe between 1952 and 1992. Its effectiveness as a barrier against foot and mouth, he claimed, had been demonstrated by the fact there was a major outbreak of the disease only a year after vaccination was discontinued.

He said: "A lot of uninfected animals have been killed

SCIENTIST: Professor Fred Brown explains his theories.

when there was an alternative. This was to vaccinate from the outside of a ring around infected premises and then work inwards. This would control it in four or five days."

Prof. Brown also claimed a machine capable of detecting the presence of foot and mouth virus in swabs taken from livestock within two hours or so had been offered to MAFF on 9th March for scientific validation, but this offer was not taken up.

He said: "You don't even have to go on to a farm to do the test. It can all be done in a lab on the back of a lorry. If the test is positive, the result comes up on a screen, in colour."

INVALUABLE

He added that the test worked for all known types of foot and mouth virus and that it would have been invaluable in fighting the current outbreak.

Dr. Simon Barteling, a specialist in the improvement and application of vaccines, was critical of the way in which DEFRA has applied the cull policy.

He said: "To prevent the disease spreading you have to find the contacts, but this has been done by just drawing circles and this is not an intelligent way. The virus is not likely to cross canals and rivers and it is the same for highways that are difficult to cross. These barriers should be taken into account when determining what is to be culled."

He attacked the way MAFF and DEFRA had conducted the slaughter process, saying it had brought a large number of contractors who were not trained in disease containment into contact with the virus.

He said: "When you are handling and lifting animals with the disease the virus gets all over the place — it

enters all corners. People doing the culling often live in rural areas and I am convinced many have been contaminated."

Discussing the arguments for and against vaccination, he said that where the disease is present in animals in a pre-clinical form, the virus can be spread on syringes, resulting in major outbreaks two or three days after injection. Additionally, it takes six or seven days for vaccination to completely remove all traces of the disease.

However, he claimed the advantages of vaccination far outweigh these drawbacks. The advantages include the fact injections can be administered by a small number of trained personnel, disease containment can be carried out in specific areas, the process is relatively cheap and farms on which animals have been slaughtered can be quickly restocked.

He said: "These things were overlooked when the EU was developing its rules on trade and they should be reconsidered. It is very important that the UK and also Holland, which is keen to have the possibility of using vaccine, should fight to change the rules."

Dr. Barteling claimed the European Commission had been keen to supply vaccine to Bulgaria, Albania, Macedonia and North Africa when foot and mouth had broken out in those areas and that vaccination had worked in every case.

DISEASE FREE

He also said the argument that a country could not be declared "disease free" if virus antibodies were present in livestock did not hold water, since animals which had been vaccinated prior to 1992 were present in a number of EU states. He estimated there were still 100,000 such animals in France and 20,000 in the Netherlands.

Epidemiologist Dr. Paul Sutmoller told the meeting the reputation foot and mouth vaccine had of being ineffective came from the period during which low quality commercial types were used in South America. Farmers, he claimed, had been reluctant to use such vaccines and so coverage had been very poor.

However, he said newer oil based vaccines were much more effective and had been used with great success in several South American countries. One example he quoted was that of Uruguay, where 10 million cattle had been vaccinated but 40 million sheep were not, yet foot and mouth was eliminated within two years.

Dr. Sutmoller claimed that he had vaccinated "thousands of sows, in all stages of pregnancy", yet had never known any to abort.

NO ILL EFFECTS

He also said British consumers had been eating meat from vaccinated cattle for more than 30 years with no ill effects, since both Argentina and Brazil had vaccinated on a large scale while exporting to Britain.

In a question and answer session held after the presentations, Prof. Brown was asked what advice he would give to the Government about vaccination.

He replied that he, Dr. Sutmoller and Dr. Barteling had already been invited to speak to the Government's chief scientist about the matter the following day, and they would repeat much of what they had said at the Penrith meeting.

While many of those at the meeting clearly favoured the use of vaccination, a number of farmers clearly had reservations, one of which was that producers in vaccinated areas might be unable to trade normally for a prolonged period.

Speaking after the meeting, John Raine, of Thornhope, Slaggyford, said: "I found it a very interesting meeting. The view of the speakers was that the regulations regarding vaccinated animals are too severe and should be altered. If they can convince the scientific experts on the regulatory body, then the whole question of vaccination is altered.

"We as farmers need two guarantees. The first is that vaccinated stock would be marketable and the second that our vaccinated stock will not be slaughtered. As Dr. Barteling pointed out, the Dutch vaccinate to live policy turned quickly to slaughter, despite farmer riots. I would hate to see that situation happen here."

He added: "If these scientists can't convince the other experts, we will have to wait for the improved vaccines that are just around the corner. We can't go through this again."

Mr. Raine has visited Holland to assess the foot and mouth policy there and spoke about the situation with Government ministers and scientists, so he has a good grasp of the issues involved.

CHANGE OF ATTITUDE

Also present at Sunday's meeting was Richard Morris, managing director of mart firm Penrith Farmers' and Kidd's, who said he had been fascinated to hear all the arguments and detected a change in the attitude of farmers.

He said: "I don't say they are fully in favour, but they do agree another mass slaughter can't be countenanced and that we need to look at vaccination.

"What is required is unbiased science and a look at what the EU position on vaccination would be."

Professor Fred Brown, a US and world authority on FMD
From The Herald Sat, 22 September 2001

8
FMD, 2001 AND THE FUTURE - A VET'S VIEW

In February 2001, foot and mouth disease arose in the north east of the country and spread so rapidly to other counties that they became isolated, no-go areas within days. None was more stricken than Cumbria and what came to be known as the Penrith spur, which took in the lovely Eden Valley. The hill farmers of Swaledale, although geographically separated by a moorland ridge that overlooks the Eden, were involved early on because many of their sheep were wintering around Appleby in a scheme introduced by English Nature to reduce grazing on the fell. A government edict was issued, whereby any farm within a three kilometre radius of an outbreak of foot and mouth had all its animals killed in an effort to prevent the spread of the disease. Many of the Eden Valley farmers lost all their animals; and some of our farmers lost up to half their flocks in the culls.

From then onward we had a ringside seat of the most comprehensive slaughter of stock ever practised in our life times. We all watched the spread of the disease, which was recorded daily on the government web site, as it marched relentlessly down the Eden Valley following the roads, despite all the so-called bio-preventative measures which were introduced to quarantine the farms. We held our breath as it approached the town of Kirkby Stephen and mourned when the herd of Shorthorns, the town's pride and joy succumbed. The townspeople were all associated in some way with the farming life of the region and all suffered in those dreadful days. People met and talked in whispers of sights they had seen and who had 'cleaned out.' We could not avoid seeing the dreadful, huge, disposal wagons as they trundled endlessly through the town with their grim burdens. Talk came of the burnings to the north, of the terrible miasma that hung over parts of the countryside, depositing fumes and a sticky substance over everything.

Inexorably, the infection progressed and we, the dwellers of neighbouring Swaledale, hoped that it would keep to the main road, pass us by, and not come over the small, narrow country road which ran the length of the dale. But, in the first week of July word came of a cull ordered on Nateby Common which meant the disease had taken a left hand fork onto the B6207 and had crossed the cattle grid onto unfenced land of the open moor! Nateby Common extends four miles up the fell to the North Yorkshire county boundary and there becomes continuous with Birkdale Common extending down into Swaledale itself. What chance did we have? The open, unfenced, moorland road, winding its way across the Pennine moors, is crossed repeatedly by the sheep which are attracted to the salt and mineral deposits on its surface.

Once long ago the road, then a rough track, was open to the wild men of the north, the Reivers, who swooped down, stole and indeed plundered. Nine Standards Rigg on the edge of Tailbridge Hill was supposedly an outpost to warn the peoples of the vales and dales of the approach of these marauders. It was as if that time had come again and the terrible paralysing fear that must have once been so common had returned to haunt us. We woke at night in the small hours and wondered just where this invisible enemy was and how far away - we truly felt about to be 'bereived.'

The farmers of the upper dale have their own stories of that time, as told in this book, which must be recorded to keep alive the memory and shout out the message that such things must never happen again.

Will foot and mouth disease (FMD) re-occur at some future date and how long before it does? The dale escaped annihilation in 2001 by a whisker, but can we guarantee that next time round we shall be so lucky and our precious heritage will not be lost forever?

Foot and mouth disease is a viral disease of cloven-hoofed animals. In many parts of the world such as Africa and South America it is endemic (that is to say, fully established) in the wild population. Thus, on those continents, it is impossible to eradicate completely, and infection is bound to spread to domesticated flocks and herds from time to time. The virus is able to mutate, rather like influenza virus strains and constant surveillance of the reservoirs of infection are needed. Strategies for protecting against or for containing the disease have been developed world wide. Some countries routinely vaccinate all their animals to protect them from ever contracting the disease. France successfully followed this practice until 1991 when it was subsequently discontinued to conform with then current EU policy, and to allow it to export to the lucrative US markets. Other countries don't vaccinate, but where there is an outbreak of the disease, they adopt a policy of culling the infected animals, and surrounding an infection by a ring fence of vaccinated animals to prevent the spread of the virus. Such policies have been successful in the wider world for many years, containing the spread of infection and so minimising the losses from foot and mouth disease outbreaks.

We must ask ourselves if so much is known about this disease why did we suffer so horrifically in 2001?

It is useful to look back to the 1967 outbreak of foot and mouth disease to see what happened in the aftermath. The then inquiry into the outbreak (Report of the Committee of Inquiry of Foot and Mouth Disease 1968) under the chairmanship of the Duke of Northumberland was a comprehensive and balanced investigation into establishing the factual evidence with respect to the disease and its control world wide. Interestingly, the cause of that particular outbreak was never definitely ascertained but was supposed to be brought in by imported infected frozen carcasses. Reading the recommendations of the Northumberland Report is eerily reminiscent of the reports produced in the aftermath of the 2001 outbreak, with regard to the role of the army and the availability of trained personnel ready to hit the ground running! One cannot help wondering just what is the usefulness of these highly expensive inquiries funded with public money if so little regard is apparently made of their findings and recommendations? Very importantly this earlier inquiry advocated that, 'contingency plans for the application of ring vaccination be kept in constant readiness,' with a recommendation for, 'the immediate application of ring vaccination to any outbreak which may occur.' Sir Anthony Cripps QC who was a member of the committee, said with remarkable prescience, that in his opinion, no matter how stringent the border controls, there was no way the risk of re-introduction of infection could be reduced to zero, and that an outbreak should be expected every twenty years or so!

Thirty years later we have experienced that predicted outbreak on a vastly greater and more damaging scale than previously. We had seemingly learnt nothing! Instead the control of the disease was dominated by the science of computer modelling. Such computer simulations are used to try to predict the spread of the disease, and to assess strategies that could be used to modify that behaviour. In the end, despite the efforts of four different teams using three different models, none of the computer simulations was, initially, able to predict the course of the disease. Because there were no models for simulating the spread of the disease in sheep, models from other contagious disease outbreaks had to be used.

Imperial College based its model on human sexual disease; a second model was on the spread of the disease from farm to farm; and the third was based on the spread of the disease in dairy cattle. Apart from the use of these inappropriate models, there was little data available when the disease first appeared, and so the teams were reduced to tracking the progress of the disease as it unfolded.

Of course, as more data became available, the models were refined and became accurate in their predictions. But that was too late; it's in the initial stages of an outbreak, when policy is being devised that predictive accuracy is most needed. Despite these criticisms, the conclusions from the modellers showed that the disease could have been equally controlled by either ring-vaccination (and the slaughter of infected animals) or by the culling of in-contact animals (S. Haywood and and G. G. Haywood, BCVA Congress Times [*Veterinary Times*] 16-18 July 2002).

In the event, culling or slaughter was preferred to ring vaccination on grounds more to do with politics and immediate commercial reasons. In so doing, decisions of a doubtful legal nature were often undertaken with regard to individual rights creating immense bitterness. Healthy stock were culled in huge numbers with insufficient provision for their disposal leaving an indelible impression on the public mind of a countryside filled with the sight of burning carcasses. Neither were health hazards from pollution of air and water courses with potential carcinogenic chemicals apparently taken into account. Furthermore, the wider interests of the community or the protection of biodiversity were either not recognised or ignored, for if this last outbreak has taught us anything it is that the practice of farming cannot be separated from the rural economy, its people and its animals. The losses from tourism alone far outweighed the actual losses on the farms and ran into billions of pounds, the final estimate being at least five billion and as high as ten billion pounds.

Further unquantifiable losses with irrevocable future implications were ignored, such as the possible effect on the hill farming agricultural ecosystems, which it has been the purpose of this book to address. Moreover, the human grief of farmers who lost the work not only of their own lifetime, but of previous generations, still reverberates in illness and despair. This latter aspect was recognised by those who compiled the 1968 report in terms that stated that,'slaughter... is a crude and primitive way of dealing with the disease. We recognise the mental anguish of those who suffer... the shattering disaster, not computable in terms of money, that it may bring to a farmer who has to see the work of a lifetime destroyed in a day.'

Have we finally learnt the lessons? There have been at least three inquiries from this last outbreak in addition to a European Union Inquiry, none of which was a truly independent public inquiry. With varying emphases their recommendations have only reinforced those of the earlier 1968 inquiry. We must ask will anyone take heed twenty years on? There have been no promises from government as to the role of vaccination.

Readers may wonder why, when vaccination has been so successful in preventing and eradicating diseases such as small pox and polio in people, it has not been used similarly in animals for the prevention of infectious disease? Of course, domesticated animals are vaccinated against a variety of killer diseases; in the companion animal or pet sector this is especially so: canine distemper is now very much a thing of the past. But with the food animals the cover against disease is less comprehensive. Reasons for this are various: sometimes the vaccines are not completely effective and can't give the cover needed. But more often they are to do with the cost of vaccinating or with misunderstandings as to the supposed dangers of using vaccinated animal carcasses for human consumption.

However, events are moving forward in this direction even as I write. At a recent conference in Buenos Aires, organised by the World Organisation for Animal Health on the control of infectious diseases by vaccination the Director General, Dr Bernard Vallat, said that in the wake of the recent foot and mouth crisis in Europe and recent influenza outbreaks in Asia, mass culling is an unacceptable way of controlling infectious and zoonotic diseases. Moreover attendees agreed that for ethical, ecological and economic reasons, it is no longer viable to control and eradicate disease outbreaks mainly by the application of mass slaughter of animals because vaccination is one of the most useful, single measures that can be used to prevent animal diseases. Importantly, this led to a series of recommendations to be implemented at the highest level to promote research efforts in vaccinology and into diagnostic tests to prevent, control, and subsequently to eradicate as far as possible animal diseases by vaccination. (*Veterinary Times*, 17 May 2004).

Let us be optimistic and hope that this will be so and that the terrible events recorded here may never recur.

Clifford and Jennie Harker at St. James's Palace, 2002

9

EPILOGUE

A round Christmas 2001 when foot and mouth disease had subsided, and as we hoped, was eradicated, Mr and Mrs Clifford Harker received an invitation from HRH Prince Charles to a reception to be held on 29 January 2002 at St James's Palace. The Prince had devised this hospitality to encourage those who had suffered during the epidemic and had included several children from farming families, traumatised by the slaughter of their stock.

It was the Prince's aim and hope that such families would not be discouraged from remaining in farming, particularly of the traditional variety of which he is so supportive. The Harkers attended the reception at which His Royal Highness in his welcoming address commented to the effect that - as a result of foot and mouth disease there was a public awareness of the important role of hefted sheep in hill farming but that no less important was the hefted farmer - meaning the tradition of farming practiced by families over successive generations. The inspiration for this book derived from this relayed speech and took place on a winter night in 2002 after a convivial evening spent at Pry House by my husband and myself, re-living with Jennie and Clifford Harker their visit to the Palace. Our friend Barbara Crossley, a local Ambleside historian with experience of oral history, readily consented to tape the memories and experiences of the four families of upper Swaledale and meetings were arranged in between lambing and shearing, interrupted by haymaking, until with patience she accumulated all the narratives to her satisfaction. Barbara transcribed these stories and early in 2003 I began writing a communicating narrative with photographs to accompany the tales - or as I felt at the time - the book began to write itself! We were fortunate to be able to persuade Barbara's childhood friend, Jocelyn Campbell of Arkengarthdale, and my friend Jenny White-Cooper of Kirkby Stephen, both professional artists, to contribute black and white illustrations to accompany the photographs, and by December the draft was all but complete.

But by December Clifford Harker's health, which had been of concern during the latter part of the summer, had declined sufficiently for him to be admitted to Middlesborough Hospital for an abdominal operation. To the distress of all who knew him, Clifford did not recover from surgery and he died on Christmas Day 2003. He was buried in the country churchyard of St Mary's, Muker on the last day of the old year. The day of the funeral was bitterly cold, the land frozen hard, lying white and still under a heavy frost which never lifted. Such was the respect and liking held for this modest and kindly man, it seemed that all the countryside had turned out to bid him farewell and the church could have been filled twice over. Indeed the service was shared by those outside who filled the small churchyard.

Standing by an old gravestone overhung with frost-rimed ivy and inscribed with the names of Charles and Isobel Alderson, nineteenth century occupants of our present house Firs (written 'Firrs'); I mused on the transience of individual lives within an unbroken continuity of past, present and future. For surely here is the heart of the matter, embodied in the life of Clifford Harker and those like him. Clifford, although over seventy years old when most men had long retired, still lived and worked his farm. He and his wife Jennie had told us that although they should be thinking of retirement they wanted to have a few more years to repair the ravages that foot and mouth disease had done to their stock and have the flock in peak condition to hand over to the next incumbent of the tenancy. This is a view shared by Clive Owen who said, 'I have to do my best to keep up the inheritance. I am honoured with the privilege to have Ravenseat for my time, and so I see it as my duty to keep it as good as I can for whoever comes after me.'

This concept of stewardship for a given period of time is something the countryman understands much better than the townsman. The land is an inheritance to be looked after and passed on in good heart to a successive generation. In acknowledging this, although there is sadness at each individual passing, there is a real future hope. The dale farmers have young families, some of whom will carry on the tradition. Indeed just as we mourn Clifford Harker, so we welcome Reuben a Christmas baby born to Amanda and Clive Owen of Ravenseat who precipitated his expected arrival by several weeks - perhaps in a hurry to claim his own inheritance!

Farming is the bedrock of civilisation and remains so; to work the land, to practice good stockmanship, to maintain productivity and sustainability for future generations is a vocation, essential for the survival of us all. We are sorry that Clifford did not live to read this book but are consoled by his having read it in draft form, up to this final epilogue that is, with some evident satisfaction at having his story told. We hope that our little book will be in some way a tribute to his life and work and will serve as an inspiration of a life well-lived to those who succeed him.

Finally we hope that the general public will re-learn and so recover something precious of their heritage. They have it in their power to protect this heritage when the voice of central control, of whatever political persuasion, attempts to impose short term solutions. For people will know that the wider picture, the fabric of the countryside, is created from an infinitude of small brush strokes that no amount of painting by numbers can emulate.

SH. 31 December 2003

GLOSSARY

Ewe - an adult female sheep.

Yow - north country term for ewe.

Gimmer - a (generally) young ewe.

Ram or tup - an adult entire male sheep.

Wether - a gelded (castrated) male sheep.

Lamb - a young (less than six months) sheep of either sex.

Hogg - a six months old to first shearing female or male sheep (i.e. ewe hogg or tup hogg).

Shearling - a sheep of either sex after having been sheared or clipped of its wool for the first time.

Geld - a barren ewe.

More farming books from Hayloft Publishing Ltd:

Yows & Cows, Mike Sanderson, 128 pages, illustrated,
ISBN 0952328208, £7.95

Not s'many Cows and a lot less Yows, Mike Sanderson, 117 pages,
illustrated, ISBN 1904524087, £9.95

Behind Chained Gates, Moira Linaker, 151 pages, illustrated,
ISBN 1904524168, £10.00

Herdwick Country Cook Book, Hugh & Therese Southgate,
180 pages, illustrated, ISBN 0954071174 (paperback £14.95) or
ISBN 0954071182 (hardback £19.95)

To Bid Them Farewell, Adam Day, 247 pages, illustrated,
ISBN 1904524109, £14.50

From Clogs and Wellies to Shiny Shoes, Miles Bolton, 215 pages,
illustrated, ISBN1904524028, £12.50

The Irish Influence, Harold Slight, 62 pages, illustrated,
ISBN0952328259, £4.95

For a full catalogue of Hayloft titles, or to order
any of the above books, please contact:

Hayloft Publishing Ltd, South Stainmore,
Kirkby Stephen, Cumbria, CA17 4DJ
tel: (017683) 42300 ~ web: books@hayloft.org.uk